Kundalini, Cerebrospinal Fluid, Multidimensional Health

Theresia Portoghese

Table of Contents:

I. Introduction
1. Brief History 4
2. Thesis Statement 7
II. Prelude – Secular and Sacred 8
III. *Pañcamayakośa* model 11
IV. *Prāṇa/Bindu* 14
V. *Nāḍī* 16
VI. *Cakras* 19
VII. *Kuṇḍalinī* 24
VIII. *Mudras/Bandhās* 26
IX. *Mudras/Bandhās Analysis* 38
X. Modern *Kuṇḍalinī* Explanations 44
XI. Cerebrospinal Fluid 48
XII. Cerebrospinal Fluid Breathing/Bandhās 52
XIII. A Story of Encephalitis 63
XIV. Conclusion 67
XV. Bibliography 69

A higher state of consciousness, able to liberate itself from the thralldom of senses, appears to be incompatible, unless we take the biological factors into account, with a physical existence in which passions and desires and the animal's needs of the body, however, restricted, exist side by side.

- Gopi Krishan, *Living with Kundalini*

1. Brief History

Many believe the first concrete representation of *yoga* comes from present-day Pakistan. Found in the Indus Valley Civilization (2500-1500 BCE), the discovery of the Pasupathi Seal surfaced in the late 1920s. The low relief clay stamp depicts an individual seated in a posture known as *sukāsana*, surrounded by animals. Branding goods from the ancient Indian valley made them distinguishable when trading with the Near Eastern civilizations of Egypt and Mesopotamia.[1] In addition to labeling market products, the logos offered a pictorial glimpse into the culture from which the goods came. It is fascinating that the northern Indian community deliberately selected the iconic image of a seated posture for a marketing logo. Is it possible the seal is the oldest example of the region self-identifying with the practice of yoga? Unfortunately, conclusive deciphering of the writing system of the Indus Valley is still in progress, and a complete understanding of the meaning behind the form is yet to be determined.[2]

Presently, we trace the germination of yoga to Hindu Vedic (*vaidika*) literature (1500-500 BCE). The primary texts of early Vedic Sanskrit literature and classic Sanskrit literature are the foundational basis for the tradition. Emulating the collectivist culture from which it manifests gave rise to philosophies and practices as diverse as the definition of the word *yóga*.[3] [4] The desire for spiritual realization inspired a wide variety of complex traditions and rituals. The

---

[1] Georg Feuerstein, Ph.D., *The Yoga Tradition, Its History, Literature, Philosophy, and Practice,* (Hohm Press, 2008), 100.
[2] Feuerstein, *The Yoga Tradition,* 100.
[3] Feuerstein, *The Yoga Tradition,* 3.
[4] *A Sanskrit English Dictionary,* Sir M. Monier-Williams, (Springfield, Virginia: Natara J. Books, 2017), 856.

binding commonality in all traditions, regardless of their ideological shifts, is all methods rely on the human body to serve as the vehicle for initiating the manifestation of an altered state of being.[5] The adaptation of the techniques, philosophies, and subsequent explanations are present in religions such as Buddhism, Hinduism, Jainism, Muslim intellectual circles, and independent yoga ascetics.[6] [7] [8] [9]

The various examples of adaptations help define distinct periods of yoga's history. One seminal text offering such classifications is *The Yoga Tradition, Its History, Literature, Philosophy, and Practice* by George Feuerstein, Ph. D. Feuerstein divides the periods of yoga's history into five sections: Foundations, Pre-Classical Yoga, Classical Yoga, Post-Classical Yoga, and the Power and Transcendence in Tantrism. Similarly, Stuart Ray Sarbacker's *Tracing the Path of Yoga, The History and Philosophy of Indian Mind-Body Discipline* also classifies yoga's history into chronological categories with the classifications of The Prehistory of Yoga: The Indus Civilization and the Vedic Tradition, Brahmanical Asceticism and Sramana Traditions, The classical Hindu Model of Yoga: Patanjala Yoga and Astangayoga, Hindu Epic, Puranic, and Scholastic Representations of Yoga, Classical Sramana Traditions of Yoga, our primary focus, The Medieval Transformation of Yoga: *Bhakti, Tantra, and Hathayoga,* and finally, Modern Traditions.[10]

---

[5] Currently, there is a great deal of debate surrounding physical postures (*āsanas*) regarding their use, the time of their introduction to the tradition of yoga, and their authenticity to the Indian culture. Although the thesis speaks to using the gross body, the focus is not on *āsanas.*
[6] Chögyal Namkhai Norbu, *Yantra Yoga, The Tibetan Yoga of Movement,* (Boulder, Colorado: Snow Lion, 2008).
[7] Christopher Key Chapple, *Yoga in Jainism,* (New York, New York: Routledge, 2017).
[8] Carl W. Ernst, *Yoga in Practice,* ed. David Gordon White (Princeton, New Jersey: Princeton University Press, 2012), 133.
[9] Feuerstein, *The Yoga Tradition,* 67-71.
[10] Stuart Ray Sarbacker, *Tracing the Path of Yoga, The History Philosophy of Indian Mind-Body Discipline,* (Albany: State of University New York Press, 2021), viii.

During the Medieval Transformation of Yoga:

> Traditions of *layayoga, kuṇḍalinīyoga,* and *haṭhayoga* developed sophisticated conceptions of an inner spiritual architecture in which the physical body is informed by the "subtle body" (*sūkṣma-śarīar*) comprised of channels (*nāḍī*) and energetic wheels (*cakra*) through which vital energy (*prāṇa*) flows. The subtle body maybe viewed as the focus for latent spiritual forces of intense energy and heat (*kuṇḍalinī caṇḍālī*), and the manipulation of *prāṇa* and the vital fluids (*bindu, bīja, rajas*) through its channels seen to facilitate rapid spiritual as well as physical transformation.[11]

In addition to addressing how the individual components collectively comprise the "inner spiritual architecture," each "sophisticated components" has a history pre-dating The Medieval Transformation of Yoga. We will explore this in further detail.

Two other fundamental philosophies adapted to the time period are raising *kuṇḍalinī* and the physical, *pranic*, mental, emotional, spiritual model known as the *pañcamayakośa* model, which originates from the *brahmānanda vallī.* Despite the evolving ideologies and techniques behind raising *kuṇḍalinī,* and the advancing ideologies for *brahmānanda vallī* turned *pañcamayakośa* model, there is a consistency in the recorded experience of *kuṇḍalinī* rising and a consistency in the use of the *brahmānanda vallī/ pañcamayakośa* model to explain the multidimensionality of the human experience.[12]

---

[11] Sarbacker, *Tracing the Path of Yoga,* 13.
[12] James Mallinson, Mark Singleton, *Roots of Yoga,* (Great Britain: Penguin Random House, UK, 2017), 179.

Although the *yoga* practices and philosophies interweave into religious traditions, their use by *yogi* ascetics fostered independently exploring the divine connection. The Medieval Transformation of Yoga's philosophies and traditions offered an alternative to highly ritualized practices replete with elaborate initiations, mantras, ritual paraphernalia, and secret mandalas. By sloughing dependency on ceremonial objects and proprietary information, spiritual development transcended reliance on religious leaders and establishments.[13] The simplified Guru guided journey of self-disciplined and independent practice manifested a renaissance of anatomical explanations for the gross and subtle bodies and the "inner spiritual architecture" became the framework for the *kuṇḍalinī* experience.

2. Thesis Statement

The focus of this thesis is to explore "the inner spiritual architecture" through the lens of the *pañcamayakośa* model concerning raising *kuṇḍalinī*. We will discuss how the components of the "spiritual architecture" (*prāṇa, nāḍī, cakra*) are directly influenced by four select techniques (*mula bandhā uḍḍīyāna bandhā, jālandhara bandhā,* and *mahabandā*). These are known as *bandhās/mudras*, which are specific to The Medieval Transformation for raising *kuṇḍalinī.* [14] Our focus will explore the mechanics of the *bandhās* and the recorded, effects.

The thesis's secondary focus is cerebrospinal fluid (CSF). Under the traditional lens of the *pañcamayakośa* model, a comparison will be made between the movement of CSF and the recorded movement *kuṇḍalinī* when engaging *mula bandhā uḍḍīyāna bandhā, jālandhara*

---

[13] James Mallinson, *Yoga in Practice,* ed. David Gordon White (Princeton, New Jersey: Princeton University Press, 2012), 257.

[14] According to the 2017 publication *A Sanskrit English Dictionary* by Sir M. Monier-Williams, page 720 defines *bandhā* as: binding, tying, a bond, tie, chain, fetter.

bandhā, and ***mahabandā***. We will also consider the benefits associated with well-regulated cerebrospinal fluid (CSF) flow and compare them to the traditional benefits gained with the practice of raising *kuṇḍalinī*. Finally, our discussion will shift to parallels between a negative *kuṇḍalinī* experience and irregular CSF flow and an anecdotal account of irregular CSF flow. The conclusion will show how understanding the philosophy and techniques of raising *kundalini* under the lens of the *pañcamayakośa* model can provide unique insights regarding function, flow and manipulation of CSF health.

II Prelude – Secular & Sacred

To begin our conversation, I would first emphasize that upholding the belief of dependency on relationships between the secular and sacred, mortal and immortal, is inherent throughout *yoga's* history. The ideology is an important point to discuss because it emphasizes the cultural perspective that divine intelligence imbues all aspects of life. The reverent approach does not segregate the body from the mind nor the body and mind from the natural surrounding it depends on. The belief stands true for both non-dualistic and dualistic manifestations of Yogic philosophy and India's ancient *Upanishads* beautifully illustrates this point. Thought to have been composed between 100 BCE to 300 CE, the non-dualistic sacred text is a collection of India's earliest philosophers' written work dedicated to postulating philosophical explanations regarding their connection, place, and purpose in the natural and supernatural planes of existence.

The *Praśna Upanishad,* Sixth *Praśna* (Concerning the Person with Sixteen parts) offers passages acknowledging,

2. To him he then said: 'Even here within the body, O friend s that Person in whom they say the sixteen parts arise.

3. He (i.e. the Person) thought to himself: "In whose departure shall I be departing? In whose resting firm, verily, shall I be resting firm?"

4. He created life (*prāṇa*); from life, faith (*śraddhā*), space (*kha*), wind, light, water, earth, sense-faculty, (*indriya*), mind, food; from food, virility, austerity, sacred saying (*mantra*), sacrifice, the worlds; and in the worlds, name (i.e. the individual).[15]

The passage also compares individuals' body parts to rivers that, on reaching the ocean, disappear; their name and form (*nāma-rūpa*) are destroyed and called "the ocean." The comparative imagery calls forth the idea of non-dualism. It serves as encouragement for one not to fear death.

6. Whereon the parts rest firm,
Like the spokes on the hub of a wheel-
Him I know as the Person to be known!
So let death disturb you not!"[16]

The intent of the philosophy is to acknowledge the symbiotic nature between philosophical and physiological practice. This point is emphasized in the *Śvetāśvatara*

[15] Robert Ernest Hume, ed. *The Thirteen Principal Upanishads, Translated from Sanskrit*, (Oxford: Oxford University Press, 1983), 389.
[16] Hume, ed. *The Thirteen Principal Upanishads*, 390.

Upanishad, under the second *adhyā*'s, "Rules and results of Yoga" admission and embrace of the natural environment can commence an elevated life that defies human perishability.

> 12. When the fivefold quality of Yoga has been produced,
> Arising from earth, water, fire, air, and space,
> No sickness, no old age, no death has he
> Who has obtained a body made out of the fire of Yoga."[17]

There is a similar emphasis on the physical melding with the spiritual in dualist Jain tradition. Jains believe that impure actions result in the physical manifestation of karma as a sticky substance known as *leśya*. "There are many different *leśyas,* and the specific type depends on the mental state behind the action that produced karma, such as whether or not the individual was motivated by anger or equanimity when performing the action."[18] Fortunately, just as the spirit can take physical form when exercising poor judgement, physical activity can result in spiritual purification of *leśya*.

> [The word] karma (in the sutra) has the other meaning *kriya*, action. The action of the body, speech and the mind are called the *yoga* (activity) of the body, speech, and mind. *Yoga* (activity) is the vibration of the soul. (5) On account of the differences of the cause this (*yoga*/activity) is divided into three kinds: body-*yoga,* speech-*yoga*, and mind-*yoga* [respectively]. [19]

[17] Hume, ed. *The Thirteen Principal Upanishads*, 398.
[18] Christopher Key Chapple, *Yoga in Jainism* (Routledge, 2016), 233, ebook.
[19] Christopher Key Chapple, *Yoga in Jainism* (Routledge, 2016), 31, ebook.

In both dualist and non-dualist religions, examples of synonymous relationships between the secular and sacred manifest to support a rich and fulfilling life experience.

III Pañcamayakośa model

Mel Robin paints an ideal image of self-cultivation inspired by a refined interception in her book entitled: *A Handbook for Yogasana Teachers; the Incorporation of Neuroscience, Physiology, and Anatomy into the Practice.* "Long before the art of dissection was practiced, the ancient yogis were able to deduce certain subtle aspects of human anatomy and physiology, through close observation of their own bodies."[20] The tradition of *yogis* using keen observation to notice subtle aspects of the human body is inherent to the culture of the practice. The *Taittirī*ya *Upaniṣad* (6 B.C.) contains the *brahmānanda vallī*, one of the earliest recorded models for quantifying subtle body observations manifesting in a physical body. Despite its early introduction to yogic literature, researchers James Mallinson and Mark Singleton note it did not reemerge in preceding literature until the 17th century. They speculate it "became so widely assimilated across traditions, this Upaniṣadic model of the body was grafted on to – or displaced other more commonly accepted conceptions of the yogic body."[21] Yogic scholar, practitioner, and teacher Francesca Michelle Gold shares in her thesis that the *pañcamayakośa* model is an adaptation of the *brahmānanda vallī* model with the introduction of the word *kośa* surfacing as early as 788-820 C.E. in *advaita* texts.[22]

---

[20] Mel Robin, *A Handbook for Yogasana Teachers, The Incorporation of Neuroscience, Physiology, and Anatomy into the Practice*, (Tuscan, Arizona: Published by Wheatmark, 2009), 201.
[21] James Mallinson, Mark Singleton, *Roots of Yoga,* (U.K.: Penguin Random House, 2017), 184.
[22] Francesca Michelle Gold, "The Influence of the *Upaniṣadic Pañcamayakośa* Schematic within Modern Yoga Therapy." (Lecture, Loyola Marymount University, Los Angeles, April 27, 2022).

Presently, the model is known as the *pañcamayakośa* model, and each of the five layers, *annamayakośha, pranamayakośha, manomayakośha, vijñānamayakośha*, and *ānandamayakośha*, maintains a distinct purpose while simultaneously influencing one another. Although the layers have taken on new names, what each layer represents, under the *Haṭha Yoga Pradīpikā,* is consistent with the *Taittirī*ya *Upaniṣad.* For example, the second *valli* of the second *anuvāka* refers to the physical-material body. It is what we use to experience life, and sustenance is an important component. In the *Haṭha Yoga Pradīpikā* this layer is known as the *pranamayakośha.*

> From food, verily, creatures are produced
>
> Whatsoever (creatures) dwell on earth.
>
> Moreover by food, in truth, they live.
>
> Moreover into it also they finally pass.[23]

The second *valli* of the third *anuvāka* refers to the vital energy that flows through the body and rides on air. In the *Haṭha Yoga Pradīpikā* this layer is known as the *pranamayakośha.*

> The gods do breathe along with breath (*prāṇa*),
>
> As also men and beasts.
>
> For truly, breath is the life (*āyus*) of beings
>
> Therefore, it is called the Life-of-all (*sarvāyuṣa*).[24]

---

[23] Hume, ed. *The Thirteen Principal Upanishads*, 284.
[24] Hume, 284.

The second *valli* of the fourth *anuvāka* refers to the mind. In the *Haṭha Yoga Pradīpikā* this layer is known as the *manomayakośha.*

> Wherefrom words turn back,
> Together with mind, not having attained-
> The bliss of Brahma he who know,
> Fears not at any time at all.[25]

The second *valli* of the fifth *anuvāka* is our intellect and intuitive sheath. In the *Haṭha Yoga Pradīpikā* this layer is known as the *vijñānamayakośha.*

> Understanding directs the sacrifice.
> And deeds also it directs.
> 'Tis understanding that all the gods
> Do worship as Brahma, as chief.[26]

Finally, sixth, seventh, eight, and ninth *anuvāka* address overcoming fear, transcending into a spiritual bliss state. In the *Haṭha Yoga Pradīpikā* these layers are collectively known as the *ānandamayakośha.* They allow us to enter a space of bliss and space in between the physical, mental, emotional, and intellectual self. *Ānandamayakośha* is the *kośha* of liberation.

> Non-existent (*a-sat*) himself does one become,
> If he knows that Brahma is non-existent.

---

[25] Hume, 285.
[26] Hume, 286.va

If one knows that Brahma exists,

Such a one people thereby know as existent.

This, indeed, is its bodily self, as of the former.[27]

Although listed in sequential order, none of the *kośhas* take precedence because all are equally essential, sacred, and divine. Additionally, the vitality of one sheath directly influences the vitality of the surrounding sheaths, and they all intermix. The multidimensional whole person model places equal importance on physical and subtle bodies, acknowledging that neglecting one will inadvertently cause other layers to atrophy. The model provides guidance when considering the vitality of an individual's "inner spiritual architecture."

Similar to the *kośa* model, the "inner spiritual architecture" refers to arising from and being sustained by food, breath, mind, intellect, and spirit. Also, like the *kośa* model, hindering the vitality of one system affects the vitality of the surrounding structures. Finally, the philosophies of the *kośas* or *Brahmānanda Vallī*, support the perspectives of the inner spiritual workings, which we will now discuss in detail.

IV Prāṇa/Bindu

The *kośa*s receive nourishment through *prāṇa*, also known as *prāṇa, bindu, bīja*, and *rajas.* Like most *yogic* things, *prāṇa* has multiple interpretations. It is both the material and incorporeal life-sustaining energy. Vasant Lad's interpretation of the life sustaining force was the electrical energy of the nervous system: "To my mind, Kundalini or the serpent power as it is called is the Vagus nerve of modern times, which supplies and controls all the important vital

---

[27] Hume, 286.īva

organs through different plexuses of the sympathetic portion of the autonomic system."[28] Indic researcher James Mallinson references the historical perspective of *prāṇa/bindu* being the manifestation and retention of sperm and the ability to retain the sperm in the head to achieve spiritual liberation.[29]

In the *Kaushitaki Upanishad* (middle of the first millennium) under the Third *Adhyāya* is the "Doctrine of *Prāṇa* (the Breathing Spirit")*.*[30] According to the ancient text *prāṇa* is not something tangible but something that rides the breath and gives animation to live.

> 3. One lives with speech gone, for we see the dumb;
> one lives with eye gone, for we see the blind;
> one lives with ear gone, for we see the deaf;
> one lives with mind gone, for we see the childish;
> one lives with arms cuts off, one lives with legs cut off, for thus we see.
> But now it is the breath spirit (*prāṇa*), even the intelligential self (*prajñātman*), that seizes hold of and animates (*ut-thā*) this body. This, therefore, one should reverence as Uktha.[31] [32]

In relation to *kuṇḍalinī* rising Mallinson notes although the "ascent through the central channel is a shared feature across yoga traditions, there is in practice, considerable diversity in conceptions of what ascends: 'the soul of self' -designated *jīva* ('life essence') or *haṃsa* ('the gander') – vital air (*prāṇa*), seed or seminal essence (*bindu*), mantric resonance, kuṇḍalinī,

---

[28] Vasant G. Rele, *The Mysterious Kundalini, The Physical Basis of Kundalini Yoga In Terms of Western Anatomy and Physiology,* (Agawam, Massachusetts: Silver Street Media, 2011), 46.
[29] James Mallinson, Mark Singleton, *Roots of Yoga,* (Great Britain: Penguin Random House, UK, 2017), 180.
[30] Hume, 320.
[31] 'The Recitation of Praise' in the ritual.
[32] Hume, 322.

Caṇḍālī.)"[33] [34] As mentioned before, the practice of *Kuṇḍalinī* cultivates a body capable of manifesting vitality through the proper distribution of *prāṇa* as expressed in the first verse of chapter three that is entitled 'Mudra and Bandha' in the *Haṭha Yoga Pradīpikā* (1350 C.E.).

> As the serpent (Sheshnaga) upholds the earth and tis mountains and woods, so *kuṇḍalinī* is the support of all yoga practices. (1)[35]

V. ***Nāḍī***

Including the concept of *prāṇa* in the underlying structural functioning of the Medieval Transformation of Yoga's inner architecture is foundational to the whole-person model; however, the philosophical roots of the concept reach back to the origins of yoga. The same is true for the idea of *nāḍī*. The *nāḍī* are the bodies innervating channels through which *prāṇa* is received. One of the earliest examples comes from the *Chāndogya Upaniṣad* (8th – 6th BCE), and the text's content is derived primarily from the *Rigveda* (c 1500 – 1000 BCE). Found in the Sixth *khaṇḍa* entitled "Passing out from the heart through the sun to immortality" verse 6 offers an early explanation of the *nāḍī:*

---

[33] The earliest mention of *kuṇḍalinī* in Jain texts is in the thirteenth-century *Mantrarājarahasya* (Pratibhāprajñā 2015a).

[34] Mallinson, *Roots of Yoga*, 179.

[35] Swami Muktibodhananda, Swami Satyananda Saraswati, *Hatha Yoga Pradipika, 2013 Golden Jubilee Edition,* (Bihar, India: Bihar School of Yoga, 2012), 279.

> 8.6.6 As to this there is the following verse: -
>
> There are a hundred and one channels of the heart. One of these passes up to the crown of the head. Going up by it, one goes to immortality. The others are for departing in various directions.[36]

The same verse repeats in the *Kaṭha Upanishad* 6.18, and the *Prasna Upaniṣad* (5-4 century BCE) also contains a passage.

> In the heart, truly, is the self (*ātman*). Here there are those hundred and one channels. To each one of these belong a hundred smaller channels. To each of these belong seventy-two thousand branching channels (*hitā*). Within them moves the diffused breath. (*vyāna*). 3.5.6
>
> Now rising upward through one of these (channels), the up-breath (*udāna*) leads in consequence of good (work) (*puṇya*) to the good world; in consequence of both, to the world of men. 3.5.7[37]

By the time the concept of the *nāḍī* reached the 15th century C.E. the composure of the *Haṭha Yoga Pradīpikā* reveals that the yogis believed the body is composed of approximately 350,000 *nāḍī* transporting organic sustenance and the immaterial essence of *prāṇa*.

> The *Shiva Samhita* says that all together there are 350,000 *nadis* in the body, the *Prapanchasara Tantra* says 300,000 and the *Goraksha Satarka* says 72,000.

[36] Hume, ed. *The Thirteen Principal Upanishads*, 267.
[37] Hume, ed. *The Thirteen Principal Upanishads*, 384.

> There are thousands upon thousands of *nadis* within the superstructure of the gross body and they distribute consciousness and prana to every atom.[38]

The three most essential *nādī* are the *idā,* the *piṇgalā*, and the *sushumnā.* These primary *nādī* orient in and around the spinal column from the coccyx to the skull.
If the *nādī* are blocked, and the *prāṇa* cannot circulate, the body becomes more suspectable to disease and dysregulation.

> The vital air does not pass in the middle channel because the *nadis* are full of impurities. So how can the stare of unmani arise and how can perfection or siddhi come about? 2.4[39]

Conversely, when an individual's *prāṇa* flows through the three hundred and fifty thousand *nādī* with ease, they can maintain their vitality.

> When all the *nadis* and *chakras* which are full of impurities are purified, then the yogi is able to retain *prana*. 2.5[40]

Although the *nādī* transport a substance that is both material and incorporeal[41] the central structure through which the central *nādī* travels is tangible. This structure is known as the *merudanda*, it stretches from the occiput to the coccyx and is comparative to the spinal column. It acts as one continual housing for the *sushumnā nādī*; however, the *sushumnā* "bifurcate(s) at

---

[38] Swami Muktibodhananda, Swami Satyananda Saraswati, *Hatha Yoga Pradipika, 2013 Golden Jubilee Edition,* (Bihar, India: Bihar School of Yoga, 2012), 158.
[39] Muktibodhananda, *Hatha Yoga Pradipika*, 158.
[40] Muktibodhananda, *Hatha Yoga Pradipika*, 160.
[41] *prāṇa, bindu, bīja, rajas*

the throat, with branches that ascend both anteriorly and posteriorly, to rejoin at the *brahmarandra,* a cavity within the skull."[42]

The *nāḍī, iḍā,* and *piṇgalā* also begin in the coccyx and travel upward along the *merudanda. Iḍā* originates at the right side of the coccyx and terminates at the left nostril and the *piṇgalā* originates at the left side of the coccyx and terminates at the right nostril. As the two *nāḍī* make their way up the spinal column, some traditions say they crisscross the *piṇgalā,* which results in a pattern like a caduceus as used by modern medicine.

It is the rising of *prāṇa* from the base of the *merudanda* through the *sushumnā nāḍī* that constitutes the beginning of a *kuṇḍalinī* experience.

> *Kuṇḍalinī* is said to be coiled like a snake. Without a doubt, one who makes the *shakti* flow obtains liberation. 3.108[43]

In traditions where the *iḍā* and *piṇgalā* intersect with the *sushumnā,* the result is the manifestation of energy centers known as *cakras.* However, we see use of *cakra* in traditions that do not have the *iḍā* and *piṇgalā* intersecting with the *sushumnā.*

VI Cakras

The *cakras* identify as wheels of energy that act as intersections "from which many other *nadi* radiate."[44] Unlike the *merudanda,* the *cakras* are not palpable. They pulsate with *prāṇa* in a whirlpool fashion and act as damns controlling the flow of life force energy to the rest of the

---

[42] Robin, *A Handbook for Yogasana Teachers*, 201.
[43] Muktibodhananda, *Hatha Yoga Pradipika*, 422.
[44] Robin, *A Handbook for Yogasana Teachers*, 201.

nādī. Similar to the *Pañcamayakośa* model, if one *cakra* is atrophied or overstimulated, it directly affects the vitality of the other *cakras.*

Traditionally speaking, when each one rotates with the proper fluidity and pace, the release of *prāṇa* is salubrious in that area of the body, which in turn supports the body's vitality. The number of *cakras* varies depending on the tradition. In the Buddhist traditions of Yantra yoga "chakras represent the inner structure of the human body, referred to in the tantric teachings as the 'vajra body' " and they typically focus on four main chakras."[45] Researcher Gavin Flood believes the use of six *cakras* first appeared in the tradition of Kaula under the 11th century C.E. work *Kubjikāmata-tantra.*[46] A full seven *cakras* model is found in *Sat Chakra Nirupana* (1526 C.E.) by Purnananda Swami. Starting at the base of the spinal column, they are *mūlādhāra, svādhiṣṭhāna, maṇipūra, anāhata, viśhuddha, añja,* and *sahasrāra.*[47]

Each *cakras* represents a multidimensional model, and like the *pañcamayakośa* model, none of the *cakras* take precedence because all are seen as equally sacred and divine. As mentioned earlier, one *cakra* directly influences the health of the surrounding *cakras,* and the imbalance of one will inadvertently cause other energy centers to destabilize. It is a recent development that the *cakras* began to include a physical element. Traditionally were considered exclusively subtle body multifaceted models. Modern guru B.K.S. Iyengar supported the idea that the *cakra* positions correlate with the location of nerve plexuses.[48] The idea of the *cakras*

---

[45] Chögyal Namkhai Norbu, *Yantra Yoga, The Tibetan Yoga of Movement,* (Boulder, Colorado: Snow Lion, 2008), 13.
[46] Gavin Flood, *The Tantric Body: The Secret Tradition of Hindu Religion,* (I.B. Tauris, 2006), 157.
[47] Purnananda Swami, *Sat-Chakra-Nirupana,* ed. Arthur Avalon, (expired copyright, accessed February 11, 2022), http://omnamo.narod.ru/chakri.html (bahaistudies.net).
[48] A nerve plexus is a network of interweaving anterior rami of spinal nerves. McKinley, *Anatomy and Physiology, An Integrative Approach*, 550.

correlating with nerve plexus is illustrated in Charles W. Leadbeater's 1927 book *The Chakras.*[49] Before the more modern interpretation, we find the *Sat Chakra Nirupana* by Purnananda Swami speaks of the *cakras* as being near the nerve plexus. Let's use the *anāhata* (heart) *cakra* as an example.

> Above that, in the heart, is the charming Lotus of the shining colour of the Bandhuka flower, with the twelve letters beginning with Ka, of the colour of vermilion, placed therein. It is known by its name of Anahata, and is like the celestial wishing-tree, bestowing even more than (the supplicant's) desire. The Region of Vayu, beautiful and with six corners, which is like unto the smoke in colour, is here.[50]

Physically we are given the *cakra's* location; however, as we begin to unpack the symbolism that comprises the energetic centers, it philosophically speaks to characteristics that support the body's physical, pranic, mental, emotional, and spiritual state. For example, in the twenty-third passage, we find a connection between meditating within the heart and dispelling fears.

---

[49] It begins with the coccyx or *muladhara* (root) *chakra* near the sacral plexus. It innervates testes and relates to L1-L3 sympathetic and S3-S4 parasympathetic. From the base we move up to L1 to the *svadhisthana.* L1 is the hypogastric plexus which innervates the pancreas, ovaries, and intestines. Next is T8, or *manipura*/celiac plexus, innervating the adrenals, diaphragm, and skin. Then T1, *anhata*/cardiac plexus, innervating the heart, thymus, lungs, and lymph glands. Moving up to C3, *vishuddha*/pharyngeal plexus, innervating thyroid, parathyroid, throat, and eyes. C1, *ajna*/nasociliary plexus, innervates the pituitary, pineal, brain and ears. Finally, the crown of the head, *sahasrana,* which fully encompasses the cerebral cortex.

[50] Purnananda Swami, *Sat-Chakra-Nirupana,* ed. Arthur Avalon, (expired copyright, accessed February 11, 2022), http://omnamo.narod.ru/chakri.html (bahaistudies.net), 22.

> Meditate within it on the sweet and excellent Pavana Bija, grey as a mass of smoke, with four arms, and seated on a black antelope. And within it also (meditate) upon the Abode of Mercy, the Stainless Lord who is lustrous like the Sun, and whose two hands make the gestures which grant boons and dispel the fears of the three worlds.[51]

In combining the philosophical interpretation with modern physiological context, the passage speaks to the condition known as Takotsubo cardiomyopathy. Experiencing intense emotional distress can cause an adverse alteration of the heart is known as broken heart syndrome or Takotsubo cardiomyopathy. The typically reversible the acute heart failure clinically presents itself as acute coronary syndrome and can result in death due to misdiagnosis. According to modern research, "Pathogenesis is complex and may involve brain-heart axis and neuro-hormonal stunning of the myocardium."[52] Presenting this information is not to imply the *anāhata chakra* (heart chakra) is something physical. Instead, it is to point out that supporting the heart's vitality is a complex multidimensional endeavor. A point eloquently acknowledged by the *Sat Chakra Nirupana.*

Additionally, strong emotions can alter the results of a heart electrocardiogram and trigger sympathetic reactions such as fight, flight, freeze, and comply, all of which directly

---

[51] Purnananda, *Sat-Chakra-Nirupana*, 8.
[52] Gupta S. Gupta MM, "Takotsubo Syndrome." *Indian Heart J.*, 70, no. 1 (2018),165-174. doi:10.1016/j.ihj.2017.09.005.

impact the ability to communicate.[53] [54] [55] Perhaps verses 25, 26, and 27 of the *Sat-Chakra-Nirupana* reference these validated phenomena. In verse 25 we find,

> "The Shakti whose tender body is like ten million flashes of lightening is in the pericarp of the Lotus in the form of a triangle (Trikona);[56]
>
> 26 "It is beautified by the Hamsa, which is like unto the steady tapering flame of a lamp in a windless place;"[57] and
>
> 27 "His senses are completely under his control. His mind in its intense concentration is engrossed in through of Brahman. His inspired speech flows like a stream of (clear) water."[58]

Modern interpretations of the *cakras*, as represented in Anodea Judith's "Chakra Balancing" kit, are more constrained and offer no original references in the material.[59] Although, this makes the multiple *cakras* attributes easier to comprehend, not including historical interpretations through the lens of the sources mitigates authentic representation. Selectively representing a multidimensional philosophy from a collectivist culture leaves room for misrepresenting the foundational underpinnings of the practice by disregarding the tradition's

---

[53] Rachel Lampert, "ECG signatures of psychological stress." *Journal of electrocardiology* vol. 48,6 (2015). 1000-5. doi:10.1016/j.jelectrocard.2015.08.005.
[54] "A systematic review on the factors affecting and the strategies to enhance effective communication between registered nurses and oncology adult patients in an inpatient setting." *JBI Library of Systematic Reviews*., 7, Issue 24 (2009). doi: 10.11124/jbisrir-2009-561.
[55] Colomer-Sánchez, Ana et al. "Anxiety Effect on Communication Skills in Nursing Supervisors: An Observational Study." *Nursing reports (Pavia, Italy)* vol. 11,2 (Apr. 2021), doi:10.3390/nursrep11020021.
[56] Purnananda, *Sat-Chakra-Nirupana*, 8.
[57] Purnananda, 8.
[58] Purnananda, 8.
[59] Anodea Judith, *Chakra Balancing Kit, A Guide to Healing and Awakening your Energy Field* (Boulder, CO: Sounds True, 2003).

historical roots. I am not advocating for treating *yoga* as irrefutable dogma. As demonstrated in this paper, doing so would be incongruent with the fundamental nature of the multifaceted discipline designed for self-evolution. However, I suggest we study the traditional philosophies and religion through a multidimensional lens to avoid overlooking key material and the misappropriation of the tradition.

VII Kuṇḍalinī

It is the combination of *prāṇa* (*aka, bindu, bīja, rajas*), *nāḍīs* (channels), and *cakra's* (energetic wheels) that comprise the "inner spiritual architecture" that supports an individual's vitality. These structures can house "latent spiritual forces of intense energy and heat" known as *kuṇḍalinī* or *caṇḍālī*.[60] The Medieval Transformation of Yoga gave rise to unique techniques for helping evoke the latent energy. The methods include specialized breath work and physically engaging the body in postures and gestures known as *bandhās/mudrās* (locks). The engagement of using the techniques is considered the act of practicing *kuṇḍalinī* because they assist with tapping into the "latent spiritual forces of intense energy and heat."[61] When these latent forces are subject to manipulation through the physical engagement, it provokes the dormant energy to "facilitate rapid spiritual as well as a physical transformation."[62] The practice of *kuṇḍalinī* cultivates a body capable of manifesting vitality through the proper distribution of *prāṇa*.

According to modern-day Yoga researcher James Mallinson one of the first textual references comparing the activation of the latent force as rising *kuṇḍalinī* is found in the

---

[60] Stuart Ray Sarbacker, *Tracing the Path of Yoga*, 13.
[61] Sarbacker, 13.
[62] Sarbacker, 13.

Goraksasataka (9-10th century B.C.E.).[63] Also known as the "Hundred Verses of Goraksa" it explains how *kuṇḍalinī* raises from the spine's base, through the spinal column, to the crown of the head. *Goraksasataka* teaches "the esoteric *sarasvaticalana"* also known as "the stimulation of Sarasvati."[64] Arousing "the *Kuṇḍalinī*, the coiled serpent goddess who lies dormant at the base of the spine in the unenlightened" is the set task for the practitioner.[65] To accomplish this goal, *Goraksasataka* suggests specific breathwork rather than use of *bandhās/mudrās* unique to the "The Medieval Transformation of Yoga" period. [66]

> (The yogin) should insert the previously trained mind and breath into the *śaṅkhinī (nāḍī)* 13 in the rod(-like) pathway at the rear by contracting the *mūlādhāra.* Breaking the three knots, he should lead (mind and breath) to the bee-cave. The *bindu* born of *nāda* goes from there to dissolution (*layam)* in the void. Through training, the yogin becomes one whose destiny is assured, chaste (*ūrdhvaretāḥ)*, supremely blissful, and free of old age and death.
>
> Or, by upward impulses of the breath (*ūrdhvaretāḥ)* (the yogin) should awaken the sleeping goddess *Kuṇḍalinī* whose abode is the base (and) whose form is like a lotus fiber. Inserting her into the Suṣumṇā (*nāḍī*) he should pierce the five *chakras.* Then he should insert the goddess into Śiva, who has the radiance of the moon. A shining faultless light, in the thousand-petalled lotus, and flood his

---

[63] James Mallinson, Mark Singleton, *Roots of Yoga,* (Great Britain, UK: Penguin Random House, 2017), 183.
[64] Mallinson, *Roots of Yoga*, 178.
[65] Mallinson, *Roots of Yoga*, 178.

[66] Mallinson, 178.

entire body, inside and out, with the nectar there. Then the yogin should think of nothing.[67]

VIII Mudras/Bandhās

Some of the sources that feature *bandhās/mudrās* for evoking *kuṇḍalinī* include the *Śiva Saṃhitā* (13-1500 C.E.), *Vivekkamārtaṇḍa* (1200 C.E.), *Haṭha Yoga Pradīpikā* (1350 C.E.), and *Gheraṇḍa Saṃhitā* (circa 1600 C.E.). Our focus will be on four the *bandhas/mudrās* ***mula bandhā*** *uḍḍīyāna bandhā, jālandhara bandhā*, and ***mahabandā*** as found in *Śiva Saṃhitā*, *Haṭha Yoga Pradīpikā*, and *Gheraṇḍa Saṃhitā*. The selection of these four ***bandhās*** and three texts is not to suggest they are more important than the other methods or texts that focus on raising *kuṇḍalinī*. The conversation has room for expansion to acknowledge all *bandhās*; however, to make our discussion more manageable, we will maintain a focus on using the texts and *bandhās*.

We will chronologically explore each of the three texts' written explanations of *kuṇḍalinī*. Then we will explore the four select *bandhās*, from their source. After introducing the individual verses, we will look for commonalities in the techniques and their associated advantages.[68] All of the passages are written as found in their printed texts.

Let's begin with the oldest of the three texts the *Śiva Saṃhitā* (13-1500 C.E.). In chapter four sloka, twenty-one through twenty-four, we find,

---

[67] James Mallinson, *The Khecarīvidyā of Ādinātha: A Critical Edition and Annotated Translation of an Early Text of Haṭhayoga*, (London: Routledge, 2007), 28-29.

[68] Some of the popular modern *Hāṭha Yoga* practices use the *bandhā*. For example, *mahabandā* is included in the 'Ashtanga Yoga Primary Series Flow' and is also under the name *ardha-paścimatāna in ardhapaścimottānāsana, and jānuśīāsana* according to *Encyclopaedia of Traditional Asanas* by editor-in-chief Dr. Manohar Laxman Gharote.

> When the sleeping Kundalini awakens through the grace
> of the guru, all the lotuses and knots are pierced. 21
> Therefore, in order to awaken the goddess sleeping at
> the opening of the gateway of Brahman, the yogi should
> make every effort to practice mudras. 22
> Mahamudra, Mahabandha, Mahavedha, Khechari,
> Jalandhara, Mulabandha, Viparitakarani, Udyana, Vajroli, 23
> And the tenth, Shaktichalana: these ten mudras are the
> very best mudras. 24[69]

In the *Haṭha Yoga Pradīpikā* (1350 C.E.) chapter three entitled, "Mudra and Bandha" we find,

> Indeed, by guru's grace this sleeping kundalini is awakened, then all the lotuses (chakras) and knots (granthis) are opened. 2
> Then indeed the sushumna becomes the pathway of prana, mind is free of all connections and death is averted. 3
> Sushumna, shoonya padavi, brahmarandhra, maha patha, shmashan, shambhavi, Madhya marga, are all said to be the same. 4
> Therefore, the goddess sleeping at the entrance of Brahma's door should be constantly aroused with all effort by performing mudra thoroughly. 5
> Maha mudra, maha bandha, maha veda, khichari, uddiyana, moola bandha, and jalandhara bandha. 6

[69] James Mallinson, ed. *The Śiva Saṁhitā* (Woodstock, New York: Yoga Vidya, 2007), 77.

> Vipareeta karani mudra, vajroli and shakti chalana, verily, these are the ten mudras which destroy old age and death. 7[70]

Finally, the *Gheraṇḍa Saṃhitā's* (circa 1600 C.E.) third lesson, "On Mūdrās" opens with,

> *Gheraṇda* said: - There are twenty-five *mudrās,* the practice of which gives success to the Yogīs. They are:- 1. *Mahā-mudra, 2. Nabho-mudrā,* 3. *Uḍḍīyāna, 4. Jālandhara, 4. Mūlabandha 6. Mahābandha, 7. Mahāvedha, 8. Khecharī, 9.Viparitakarī, 10. Yoni, 11. Vajroṇi, 12. Śaktichālanī, 13. Tāḍāgī, 14. Māṇḍukī, 15.Śāmbhavī, 16. Pancadhāraṇā (five dhāraṇās), 21. Aśvinī, 22. Pśāśinī, 23. Kākī, 24, Mātaṅgṅī and 25. Bhujaṅginī.*[71]

Out of the three texts, the *Gheraṇḍa Saṃhitā* is the only text to offer general benefits associated with the *bandhā/mūdrā.* They are provided as part of the third lesson, "On *Mūdrās"* under the title "The Advantages of Practicing Mūdrās."

> *Maheśwara,* when addressing his consort, has recited the advantages of *Mūdrās* in these words: "O Devi! I have told you all the *Mūdrās*; their knowledge leads to adeptship (sic). It should be kept secret with great care, and should not be taught indiscriminately to everyone e. This gives happiness to the *Yogīs and* is not to be easily attained by the maruts (gods of air) even."[72]

---

[70] Muktibodhananda, *Hatha Yoga Pradipika*, 499.
[71] Rai Bahadur Srisa Chandra Vasu, ed. *Gheraṇḍa Saṁhitā* (Varanasi, India: Indian Mind, 2012), 43.
[72] Vasu, *Gheraṇḍa Saṁhitā*, 44.

Each description of the *bandhā/mūdrā's* defines its characteristics in the descriptions. We will begin with the descriptions for the four selected *bandhās* (*mula bandhā uḍḍīyāna bandhā, jālandhara bandhā*, and *mahabandā*) chronologically starting with the *Śiva Saṃhitā*. The order of the *bandhās* and text is written as it is presented in the sources.

2. Mahā bandha:

> While in Mahabanda, place the foot that is extended upon the thigh. Contract the anus and yoni and make the apana move upwards. 37
> Join prana with samana and make it face downwards, the wise yogi should apply this in order to make prana and apana move upwards. 38
> The Mahabanda that I have taught leads the way to perfection. All the yogi's go from the network of nadis to the head. 39
> One should take great care to practice this with both feet alternately. Through practice, the wind enters the Sushumna. 40
> It enters the body, make the skeleton strong, and fills the yogi's heart. These things arise in the yogi. 41
> Using this bandha, the lord of yogis unties prana and apana and accomplishes all that he desires in the three worlds. 42[73]

Jalandharabandha:

> Constrict the network of vessels in the neck and place the chin on the chest. This is called Jaladharabandha. It is precious even to the gods. 60

[73] James Mallinson, ed. *The Śiva Saṁhitā* (Woodstock, New York: Yoga Vidya, 2007), 81.

In living beings, the fire situated at the naval drinks the abundance of nectar pouring from the thousands-petaled lotus. That is why one should apply this bandha. 61

By applying this bandha, the wise yoga drinks the nectar himself. He becomes immortal and has fun in the three worlds. 62

The Jalandhara bandha grants perfection to adepts. The yogi desirous of perfection should carry out the practice regularly. 63[74]

Mulabandha:

Press the anus tightly with the heel. Forcefully pull the apana and gradually raise it. 64

This makes Mulabandha. It destroys decrepitude and death and is sure to unite apana and prana. 65

By applying this bandha, Yonimudra is easily perfected. When Yonimudra is perfected, there is nothing on earth that one cannot master. 66

By grace of this mudra, the yogi sitting in Padmasana conquers the wind and leaves the ground to dwell in the sky. 67[75]

Udyanabandha:

The yogi should stretch the region above and below the navel backwards. The is Udyanabandha. It destroys all one's many sorrows. 72

---

[74] Mallinson, ed. *The Śiva Saṁhitā*, 88.
[75] Mallinson, 90.

He should stretch it behind the stomach and about the navel. In this text this bandha is called Udyana. It is a lion against the elephant of death. 73
The navel of the yogi who regularly performs it four times a day is purified, and the wind is mastered. 74
Practicing it for six months, the yogi is sure to conquer death. The fire in his stomach burns brightly and there is an increase in his vital fluids. 75
The body easily becomes perfected through using it and the yogi's diseases are sure to be eliminated. 76
The wise yogi should obtain this extremely precious bandha from a guru and practice it in a comfortable place where there are no people. 77[76]

Now we will explore the four *bandhas* as found in the *Haṭha Yoga Pradīpikā* under chapter three.

Maha bandha:

Press the heal of the left foot in the perineum/vagina and place the right foot on the left thigh. 19
Thus, breathing in, bring the chin to the chest (*jalandhara bandha*), contract the perineal/cervical region (moola bandha) and concentrate on the eyebrow center (*shambhavi mudra*). 20
Having retained the breath as long as comfortable, exhale slowly. Once completing the practice on the left side, practice again on the right side. 21

[76] Mallinson, ed. *The Śiva Saṁhitā*, 91.

Some are of the opinion that the throat lock (*jalandhara bandha*) is unnecessary, and it is sufficient to keep the tongue against the front teeth. 22
This stops the upward movement of energy in the nadis. Verily this maha bandha is the bestower of great siddhis. 23
Maha bandha frees one from the bonds of death, makes the three nadis unite in ajna chakra and enables the mind to reach the sacred seat of Shiva, Kedara. 24[77]

Uddiyana Bandha:

Uddiyana bandha is so-called by the yogis because through its practice the prana (is concentrated at one point and) rises through sushumna. 55
The bandha described is called the rising or flying bandha, because through its practice, the great bird (*shakti*) flies upward with ease. 56
Pulling the abdomen back in and making the navel rise is uddiyana bandha. It is the lion which conquers the elephant, death. 57
Uddiyana is easy when practiced as told by the guru. Even an old person can become young when it is done regularly. 58
The region above and below the navel should be drawn backward with effort. There is not doubt that after six months of practice, death is conquered. 59
Of all the bandhas, uddiyana is the best. Once it is mastered, mukti or liberation occurs spontaneously. 60[78]

[77] Muktibodhananda, *Hatha Yoga Pradipika*, 302.

[78] Muktibodhananda, *Hatha Yoga Pradipika*, 332-339.

Moola Bandha:

> Pressing the perineum/vagina with the heel and contracting the rectum so that the apana vayu moves upward is moola bandha. 61
>
> By contracting the perineum, the downward moving apana vayu is forced to go upward. Yogis call this moola bandha. 62
>
> Press the heel firmly against the rectum and contract forcefully and repeatedly, so that the vital energy rises. 63
>
> There is not doubt that by practicing moola bandha, prana and apana, and nada and bindu are untied, and total perfection attained. 64
>
> With constant practice of moola bandha, prana and apana unite, urine and stool are decreased and even an old persons become young. 65
>
> Apana moves up into the region of fire (*manipura chakra, the naval center*), then the flames of the fire grow, being fanned by apana vayu. 66
>
> Then, when apana and fire meet with prana, which is itself hot, the heat in the body is intensified. 67
>
> Through this, the sleeping kundalini is aroused by the extreme heat, and it straightens itself just as a serpent beaten with a stick straightens and hisses. 68
>
> Just as a snake enters its hole, so kundalini foe into the brahma nadi. Therefore, the yogi must always perform moola bandha. 69[79]

[79] Muktibodhananda, *Hatha Yoga Pradipika*, 340.

Jalandhara Bandha:

> Contracting the throat by bringing the chin to the chest is the bandha called jalandhara. It destroys old age and death. 70
> The is jalandhara bandha which catches the flow of nectar in the throat. It destroys all throat ailments. 71
> Having done jalandhara bandha by contracting the throat, the nectar does not fall into the gastric fire and the prana is not agitated. 72
> By firmly contracting the throat, the two nadis, ida and pingala are paralyzed and the sixteen adharas of the middle chakra are locked. 73
> By contracting the perineum, performing uddiyana and locking ida and pingala with jalandhara, sushumna becomes active. 74
> By this means the prana and breath become still. Thus death, old age and sickness are conquered. 75
> The great siddhas practice these three best bandhas. Of all the sadhanas in hatha yoga and tantra, the yogis know this practice (maha bandha). 76
> The nectar which flows from the moon has the quality of endowing enlightenment, but it is completely consumed by the sun, incurring old age. 77[80]

Finally, our summary will conclude with the *Gheraṇḍa Saṃhitā* as found in the third lesson.

Uḍḍīyāna-Bandha:

> Contract the bowls equably about the below the navel towards the back, so that the abdominal viscera may touch the back. He who practices this *Uḍḍīyāna*

[80] Muktibodhananda, *Hatha Yoga Pradipika*, 352-362.

(Flying up), without ceasing, conquers death. The Great Bird (Breath), by this process, is instantly forces up into the *Suşumnā,* and flies (moves) constantly therein only.

Of all *Bandhanas,* this is the best. The complete practice of this makes emancipation easy. 3[81]

Jālandhara:

Contracting the throat, place the chin on the chest. This is called *Jālandhara.* By this *Bandha* the sixteen *Ādhāras* are closed. This and the *Mahā-mudrā* destroy death.

The *Jālandhara* is a success-giving and well-tried *Bandha*; he who practices it for six months, becomes an adept without doubt. 4[82]

Mūlabandha:

Press with the heel of the left foot the region between the anus and the scrotum and contract the rectum; carefully press the intestines near the naval on the spine; and put the right heel on the organ of generation of pubes. This is called *Mūlabandha*, destroyer of decay.

The person who desires to cross the ocean of Existence, let him go to a retired place, and practice in secrecy this *Mūdrā.* By the practice of it, the *Vāyu* (*Prāṇa*)

---

[81] Vasu, *Gheraṇḍa Saṁhitā*, 45.
[82] Vasu, *Gheraṇḍa Saṁhitā*, 46.

is controlled undoubtedly; let one silently practice this, without laziness and with care. 5[83]

Mahābandha:

Close the anal orifice by the heel of the left foot, press that heel with the right foot carefully, move slowly and slowly the muscles of the rectum, and slowly contract the muscles of the yoni or perineum (space between the anus and organ): restrain the breath by *Jālandhara.* This is called *Mahābandha.*

The *Mahābandha* is the Greatest *Bandha*; it destroys decay and death: by virtue of this *Bandha* a man accomplishes all his desires. 6[84]

Although the text offer thorough instructions on engaging the *bandhās,* and their benefits, there is no information regarding the position one should take when performing the techniques. The omission of the crucial component speaks to the oral tradition from which the practice originates. It also is an example of how the texts do not always address that which was perceived to be common knowledge.[85] Swami Muktibodhananda's *Hatha Yoga Pradipika* confirm through illustrations and additional instruction that the *bandhās* should be engaged while seated. Additionally, there are references to the advantageous nature of an erect seated posture and

---

[83] Vasu, *Gheraṇḍa Saṁhitā*, 47.
[84] Vasu, *Gheraṇḍa Saṁhitā*, 48.
[85] As discussed on page 11, despite "five (kośas) sheaths" early introduction to yogic literature, researchers James Mallinson and Mark Singleton note it remained unmentioned until the 17th century. They speculate it "became so widely assimilated across traditions, this Upaniṣadic model of the body was grafted on to – or displaced other more commonly accepted conceptions of the yogic body." Perhaps the same is true regarding the instruction to sit in an upright position.

"trained breath" in earlier works. For example, the *Śvetāśvatara Upanishad* (1000-1 B.C.) under the "Rules and Results of Yoga- 2.6.8-9" states,

> 8. Holding his body steady with the three (upper parts2) erect,
> And causing the sense with the mind to enter into the heart,
> A wise man with the Brahma-boat should cross over
> All the fear-brining streams.
> 9. Having repressed his breathings here in the body, and having his movements checked.
> One should breathe through his nostrils with diminished breath.
> Like a chariot yoked with vicious horses,
> His mind the wise man should remain undistractedly.[86]

Similarly, the *bhakti* text the *Yoga Sūtra's* of *Pātañjali* (early centuries C.E.) made popular modern-day postural yoga, offers a philosophical perspective stemming from the physiological engagement of posture and breath in *"Sādhana Pāda."* Verse 2.46 advises that "*āsana* is steadiness and ease."[87] Verses 2.49-2.55 offer the benefits of controlling the breath.

> 2.49 Being in this, there is control of the breath, which is the cutting off the motion of the inbreath and outbreath.
> 2.50 Its fluctuations are external, internal, and suppressed; it is observed according to time, place, and number, and becomes long and subtle.
> 251. The fourth is withdrawal from external and internal conditions (of breath).

---

[86] Hume, *The Thirteen Principal Upanishads*, 398.
[87] Christopher Key Chapple, *Yoga and the Luminous, Patañjali's Spiritual Path to Freedom* (Delhi, India: Divine Books, 2008), 179.

2.52 Thus, the covering of light is dissolved.

2.53 And there is fitness of the mind-power for concentrations.

2.54 Inwardness of the senses is the disengagement from conditions if in imitation of the won-form mind.

2.55 Then arises the utmost command of the senses.[88]

VIII Mudras/Bandhās Analysis

The exploration of earlier references adds contextualization to the practice of *Kuṇḍalinī* and allows for a broader picture of what it entails. Additionally, it is easy to see that the independent use of *mula bandhā, uḍḍīyāna bandhā,* or *jālandhara bandhā* all assist in evoking *kuṇḍalinī* in advantageous ways; however, it is their simultaneous engagement as *mahabandā* that intensifies the potency of the techniques. Let's go back and summarize the *kuṇḍalinī* activation method for each *bandhā* and the associated benefits.

According to the *Śiva Saṃhitā, mula bandhā's* activation is

> Press the anus tightly with the heel. Forcefully pull the apana and gradually raise it. 64 "pressing well the anus with the heel, (and) forcibly draw(ing) upwards.[89]

The *Haṭha Yoga Pradīpikā* is similar.

> Pressing the perineum/vagina with the heel and contracting the rectum so that the apana vayu moves upward is moola bandha. 61 By contracting the perineum, the

[88] Chapple, *Yoga and the Luminous*, 180-181.
[89] Mallinson, ed. *The Śiva Saṁhitā*, 90.

> downward moving apana vayu is forced to go upward. Yogis call this moola bandha. 62[90]

And the *Gheraṇḍa Saṃhitā* also makes mention of using the heel.

> "Press with the heel of the left foot the region between the anus and the scrotum and contract the rectum; carefully press the intestines near the naval on the spine; and put the right heel on the organ of generation of pubes. This is called *Mūlabandha*, destroyer of decay.[91]

The similarities found in the three texts for ***mula bandhā*** make it clear that pressing the heel into the anus/perineum/vagina/area between the anus and scrotum helps activate the *kuṇḍalinī* energy and stimulate it to rise. Just as the three texts share similarities in technique, they also claim similar benefits. For example, in the *Śiva Saṃhitā,* there is an emphasis on *prāṇa* and *apāṇa* uniting, conquering the wind, and dwelling in the sky.[92] In the *Haṭha Yoga Pradīpikā,* the emphasized benefits include *prāṇa* and, *apāṇa* uniting urine and stool decreasing, and heat of the navel center and overall body increasing.[93] The *Gheraṇḍa Saṃhitā* grants the practitioner a reprieve from existence by evoking the ability to control the bodies *prāṇa.*[94]

Uḍḍāna bandhā's activation according to *Śiva Saṃhitā*

> The yogi should stretch the region above and below the navel backwards. The is Udyanabandha. It destroys all one's many sorrows. 72

---

[90] Muktibodhananda, *Hatha Yoga Pradipika*, 340.
[91] Vasu, *Gheraṇḍa Saṁhitā*, 47.
[92] Mallinson, ed. *The Śiva Saṁhitā*, 90.
[93] Muktibodhananda, *Hatha Yoga Pradipika*, 340.
[94] Vasu, *Gheraṇḍa Saṁhitā*, 47.

> He should stretch it behind the stomach and about the navel. In this text this bandha is called Udyana. It is a lion against the elephant of death. 73[95]

Haṭha Yoga Pradīpikā

> Pulling the abdomen back in and making the navel rise is uddiyana bandha. It is the lion which conquers the elephant, death. 57[96]

Gheraṇḍa Saṃhitā

> Contract the bowls equably about the below the navel towards the back, so that the abdominal viscera may touch the back.[97]

The three passages for Uḍḍāna bandhā's activation all focus on the manipulation of the viscera, thus stretching the area around the navel and stomach. Also, the three texts share similarities in technique as well as benefits. For example, the *Śiva Saṃhitā* the method is thought to destroy sorrows, master internal winds, conquer death, increase vital fluids and eliminate disease.[98] In the *Haṭha Yoga Pradīpikā* the emphasized benefits include conquering death, youthfulness, and liberation.[99] The *Gheraṇḍa Saṃhitā* grants conquering death and accessible emancipation.[100]

---

95 Mallinson, ed. *The Śiva Saṁhitā*, 91.
96 Muktibodhananda, *Hatha Yoga Pradipika*, 332.
97 Vasu, *Gheraṇḍa Saṁhitā*, 45.
98 Mallinson, ed. *The Śiva Saṁhitā*, 91.
99 Muktibodhananda, *Hatha Yoga Pradipika*, 332-339.
100 Vasu, *Gheraṇḍa Saṁhitā*, 45.

Jālandhara bandhā's activation according to *Śiva Saṃhitā*

> Constrict the network of vessels in the neck and place the chin on the chest. This is called Jaladharabandha. It is precious even to the gods. 60[101]

Haṭha Yoga Pradīpikā

> Contracting the throat by bringing the chin to the chest is the bandha called jalandhara. It destroys old age and death. 70[102]

Gheraṇḍa Saṃhitā

> Contracting the throat, place the chin on the chest.[103]

The similarities found in the three texts for *jālandhara bandhā* all emphasize constricting the vessels in the neck by placing the chin on the chest. The three texts also share similarities in benefits. In the *Śiva Saṃhitā* there is the emphasis the lock prevents flowing "nectar" from the head immortal.[104] The *Haṭha Yoga Pradīpikā* also emphasizes the use of the lock to prevent nectar from falling into the "gastric fire," thus avoiding the "agitation of prana." Additionally, the lock paralyzes "the two nadis, ida, and pingala" and locks "the sixteen adharas"[105] of the middle chakra." This, in turn activates the *sushumna* (central) so sickness, old age, and death are

---

101 Mallinson, ed. *The Śiva Saṁhitā*, 88.
102 Muktibodhananda, *Hatha Yoga Pradipika*, 352.
103 Vasu, *Gheraṇḍa Saṁhitā*, 46.
104 Mallinson, ed. *The Śiva Saṁhitā*, 88
105 For more on the sixteen adharas see page 54.

conquered.[106] The *Gheraṇḍa Saṃhitā* also mentions the closure of "the sixteen adharas" in addition to avoiding death and gaining adeptness.[107]

Mahabandhā's activation according to *Śiva Saṃhitā*

> While in Mahabanda, place the foot that is extended upon the thigh. Contract the anus and yoni and make the apana move upwards. 37
>
> Join prana with samana and make it face downwards, the wise yogi should apply this in order to make prana and apana move upwards. 38[108]

Haṭha Yoga Pradīpikā

> Press the heal of the left foot in the perineum/vagina and place the right foot on the left thigh. 19
>
> Thus, breathing in, bring the chin to the chest (*jalandhara bandha*), contract the perineal/cervical region (moola bandha) and concentrate on the eyebrow center (*shambhavi mudra*). 20
>
> Having retained the breath as long as comfortable, exhale slowly. Once completing the practice on the left side, practice again on the right side. 21
>
> Some are of the opinion that the throat lock (*jalandhara bandha*) is unnecessary, and it is sufficient to keep the tongue against the front teeth. 22[109]

---

[106] Muktibodhananda, *Hatha Yoga Pradipika*, 352-362.
[107] Vasu, *Gheraṇḍa Saṁhitā*, 46.
[108] James Mallinson, ed. *The Śiva Saṁhitā*, 81.
[109] Muktibodhananda, *Hatha Yoga Pradipika*, 302.

Gheraṇḍa Saṃhitā

> Close the anal orifice by the heel of the left foot, press that heel with the right foot carefully, move slowly and slowly the muscles of the rectum, and slowly contract the muscles of the yoni or perineum (space between the anus and organ): restrain the breath by *Jālandhara.* This is called *Mahābandha.*[110]

Of the four bandhās, *mahābandhā* has the most variation in terms of technique. For example, *The Śiva Saṃhitā* does not specify which heel is placed in the area of the perineum/anus or which foot to place on top of the thigh.[111] The *Haṭha Yoga Pradīpikā* instruct placement of the left heal in the "perineum/vagina" and the right foot "on the left thigh."[112] Similar to The *Haṭha Yoga Pradīpikā, Gheraṇḍa Saṃhitā,* also instructs use of the left heel in the "anal orifice"; however, the right foot is to carefully assist in pressing the left heal in the "anal orifice."[113] Finally, only the *Haṭha Yoga Pradīpikā* offers the alternative keeping "the tongue against the front teeth" as an alternative to *jālandhara bandhā.*[114]

Apart from the varying instruction, the benefits are similar. The *Śiva Saṃhitā* emphasizes the upward lift of *prāṇa* and *apāṇa* to make the skeleton strong, fill the heart, and fulfill desires.[115] The *Haṭha Yoga Pradīpikā* stops the movement of the *nāḍī* so they can unite at "ajna chakra" thus reaching "the sacred seat of Shiva, Kedara" and avoiding death.[116] The *Gheraṇḍa*

---

110 Vasu, *Gheraṇḍa Saṁhitā*, 48.
111 Mallinson, ed. *The Śiva Saṁhitā*, 81.
112 Muktibodhananda, *Hatha Yoga Pradipika*, 302.
113 Vasu, *Gheraṇḍa Saṁhitā*, 48.
114 Muktibodhananda, *Hatha Yoga Pradipika*, 302.
115 Mallinson, ed. *The Śiva Saṁhitā*, 81.
116 Muktibodhananda, *Hatha Yoga Pradipika*, 302.

Saṃhitā claims the *bandhā* "destroys decay and death" allowing by virtue a man to accomplish "all his desires."[117]

In reviewing the *bandhā's,* it is clear the engagement of the practice is a whole-person experience involving all the layers of the *Pañcamayakośa* model. For example, the physical body enables the engagement of the *bandhās*, engagement of the *bandhās* stills the breath which in turn controls the effects of the *prāṇa.*[118] The effects lead to attributes such as mental adeptness,[119] emotionally free of "sins and sorrows"[120], and emancipation.[121] We will now turn our attention to cerebrospinal fluid and explore the possibility of using it as a vehicle for *Kuṇḍalinī* awakening.[122]

X Modern Kuṇḍalinī Explanations

I want to begin the conversation regarding cerebrospinal fluid by emphasizing that the traditional practice of raising *Kuṇḍalinī* by use of breath and *bandhās* is ultimately for spiritual enlightenment. Also, the act of learning how to evoke *Kuṇḍalinī* fully is typically exclusive to dedicated initiates of a particular discipline.[123] Our discussion does not cover the full scope of the practice no more than reading the recipe to bake a cake allows for the experience of eating it; However, I propose studying the ancient techniques from the perspective of their philosophical

---

[117] Vasu, *Gheraṇḍa Saṁhitā*, 48.
[118] Muktibodhananda, *Hatha Yoga Pradipika*, 340.
[119] Vasu, *Gheraṇḍa Saṁhitā*, 46.
[120] Mallinson, ed. *The Śiva Saṁhitā*, 91.
[121] Vasu, *Gheraṇḍa Saṁhitā*, 45.
[122] It was after reading *Living with Kundalini, The Autobiography of Gopi Krishna* that I realized that many have drawn parallels between CSF and *Kuṇḍalinī.* Additionally, there are recordings of spontaneous *Kuṇḍalinī* awakenings, which did not involve breathwork, or *bandhās.*
[123] Norbu, *Yantra Yoga,* 9.

roots creates a potential for advancing our understanding of whole-person models. Additionally, the experiential organic links that connect the modern practitioner to the ancient *yogi* remain in place despite advancements in our understanding of anatomy and physiology. In other words, if there is a connection between arising *kuṇḍalinī* and cerebrospinal fluid (CSF), the ancient practice may better offer insights into understanding CSF's flow and function.

The desire to elevate our understanding of the *kuṇḍalinī* experience through the lens of physiological explanations is not a unique pursuit. Physiologist Vasant G. Rele's 1929 publication *The Mysterious Kundalini, The Physical Basis of the "Kundalini (Hatha) Yoga" In Terms of Western Anatomy and Physiology* encapsulates and ascribes the *Kundalini* experience to one nerve in the body, the vagus nerve. "To my mind, Kundalini, or the serpent power as it is called is the Vagus nerve of modern times, which supplies and controls all "the important vital organs through different plexuses of the sympathetic portion of the autonomic system."[124]

Additionally, modern-day *Hāṭha* yoga researcher James Mallinson's anatomical perspective is a retroactive interpretation of the incentive behind raising *Kuṇḍalinī*. Mallinson argues that the 13th century male Yogis attributed their life's vitality to fluid known as "*bindu*" or sperm.[125] Manifesting in the head and drawn down into the body by gravity, the fluid came to symbolize the elixir of life. The ability to retain the *bindu* in the body, ideally in the head, is directly correlated with longevity. The result is achieving spiritual liberation.[126]

Most notably, yogi, scholar, and humanitarian Gopi Krishna (1903-1984) advocated, wrote, and spoke on raising *Kuṇḍalinī*. The insight is about on his personal experience with a *Kuṇḍalinī* awakening meditating for three hours a day every morning for seventeen years. The

---

124 Vasant G. Rele, *The Mysterious Kundalini*, 46.
125 Mallinson, *Roots of Yoga*, 180.
126 Mallinson, 180.

event marked the beginning of his journey to understand the phenomena better and navigate the physical, mental, emotional, and spiritual benefits and repercussions of unleashing the energetic force. After Gopi's Gopi's awakening, he spent years working through the process of letting the latent energies transform his body and mind. The process led him to believe he was "suffering from hallucinations" an alternate reality that left him feeling "exhausted and spent."[127] He also "lost love for my (his) wife and children" saw the "world through a haze", and lost interest in food often leaving "his plate untouched." [128] As a result of the experience, his body and memory became weaker as his anxieties heightened.[129] Through time, some guidance, and trial and error, Gopi shared his experiences and techniques for counterbalancing the conditions resulted in his enlightened state.[130] This inspired 'The Kundalini Research Foundation.' Founded by Gopi Krishna and his publicist Gene Kieffer, the organization led to the creation of other groups supporting the effort of studying *Kuṇḍalinī.* They include the Institute for Consciousness Research,[131] Emerging Sciences Foundation,[132] Patanjali Kundalini Yoga Care,[133] Kundalini Research Network,[134] and yes, there is a *Kuṇḍalinī* Facebook group.[135]

Harvard educated Dr. Mauro Zappaterra wrote his thesis and subsequent papers focusing on proteomic analysis of CSF, how it provides a niche for neural progenitor cells and in adult rats promotes neural stem cell proliferation. He shared the following on his research at the 2019 Kundalini Symposium.

---

[127] Krishna, *Living with Kundalini*, 146.
[128] Krishna, 148-149.
[129] Krishna, 150-151.
[130] Krishna, 148-149.
[131] icrcandad.org
[132] www.emergingsciences.org
[133] Kundalinicare.com
[134] www.kundalininet.org
[135] www.facebook.com/kundalini-140971995120

> Marriage of the pineal and pituitary gland energies come to form a perfect harmony. It is my believe that this is the place of the birth of the "I Am" in physical form. Where through dispersion of the energy within the fluid our entire brain is simultaneously bathed with the differentiated energy from the source providing the synchronous unified experience and awareness of our true essence. [136]

The focus of this thesis is not to ascribe a *Kuṇḍalinī* experience to something anatomical like Vasant G. Rele or offer a historical explanation regarding raising *Kuṇḍalinī*, like Mallinson. And although Gopi asserts, "The awakening of kundalini and its ascent to *sahasrara* is a strictly biological phenomenon, as amenable to study and investigation as any other phenomenon of nature."[137], and Dr. Zappaterra's work may be a starting point for explaining the phenomenon, as a yogic scholar and yoga therapist in training, I believe understanding the biology and kinesiology behind the techniques for raising *kuṇḍalinī* are just as meaningful as unleashing the latent energy. Having a heighted understanding of the process may offer insights for shifting the subtle body model (mind, emotions, and spirit) and conversely, understanding the subtle body influences on the physical body. Investigating the phenomena through the multidimensional *pañcamayakośa* lens creates an avenue to understanding how the multiple factors support one another. It also emphasizes how the imbalance of one layer directly influences the tensegrity of the entire model and influences the behaviors of the other layers.

---

[136] Mauro Zappaterra, "The Cerebrospinal Fluid and I AM." YouTube. 2019. Educational Video, 31:33. https://youtu.be/oPU0DGjK3XA.

[137] Gopi Krishna, *Living with Kundalini, The Autobiography of Gopi Krishna*, (Boston, Massachusetts; Shambhala: 1993), 357.

My first exposure to studying the western practice of *Kuṇḍalinī*,[138] as established by Yogi Bhajan, was through my teacher, Hari Simran Kaur Khalsa. She instructed us to engage *mula bandhā* to awaken the latent *Kuṇḍalinī* energy at the base of our spines. Her reasoning being "moving cerebrospinal fluid (CSF) from the base of the spine up to the head further bastes the brain in CSF for physical, mental, and emotional health."[139] The image of *mula bandhā* being a hand squeezing the base of my spine, my spine turning into the shaft of a turkey baster and a fountain of CSF basting my brain never left me. I was left wondering, is it physically possible to manipulate CSF using of the *bandhās*? What is the role of CSF? And how does CSF support our health and wellness?

XI Cerebrospinal Fluid

Sometimes referred to as the "nourishing liquor" of the brain, cerebrospinal fluid is vital to the survival of an individual.[140] Produced in cavities found in the center of the brain, the distilled liquid is from the cerebral blood. Just as the earth filters the rising water of a seep spring, "simple cuboidal epithelium (which) surrounds clusters of fenestrated capillaries allowing for the filtration of plasma."[141] The result is oozing ultrafiltrate plasma into the brain's ventricles. The centrally located life-sustaining aquifer, known as the choroid plexus, produce 400 to 600 ml

---

[138] The word *Kuṇḍalinī* is used to name a style of yoga popular in America and established by Yogi Bhajan. The organization is redefining itself in the wake of scandal pertaining to Bhajan.
[139] Hari Simran Kaur Khalsa, group conversation, 2010.
[140] Ian Johnston, Brian Owler, and John Pickard, "Introduction," *The Pseudotumor Cerebri Syndrome: Pseudotumor Cerebri, Idiopathic Intracranial Hypertension, Benign Intracranial Hypertension and Related Conditions* (Cambridge: Cambridge University Press, 2007), 1-5, ebook.
[141] L.N. Telano, S. Baker, *Physiology, Cerebral Spinal Fluid* (Treasure Island, FL: State Pearls Publishing, July 4, 2020), www.ncbi.nlm.nih.gov/books/NBK519007/.

of cerebrospinal fluid per day. As a result, it completely renews four to five times within 24 hours for an average adult. [142]

Typically, the production rate of CSF depends on the cerebral blood flow pressure. Higher CSF pressure results in less of a pressure variable between "the capillary blood in choroid plexuses and CSF. An increase in CSF decreases the amount of cerebral blood that moves into the choroid plexus to become CSF."[143] "The autonomic nervous systems influence choroid plexus CSF secretion, with activation of the sympathetic nervous system increasing secretion and the parasympathetic nervous system decreasing it."[144] Regulation of the interstitial fluid creates a homeostatic environment for the brain, imperative for normal neural function. Additionally, the regulated pressure results in a hydraulic system that provides the brain and spinal column buoyancy against gravity and offers shock-absorbing protection.

In addition to playing a mechanical role in health and wellness, the ultrafiltrate of plasma supplies the body with growth factors, iodine, vitamins B1, B12, folate, beta 2, microglobulin, arginine, vasopressin, nitric oxide, and a higher concentration of sodium and chloride than blood plasma, which is circulated by CSF.[145]

Currently, the traditional circulation pattern of CSF is under scrutiny. For decades, teachings on the production and flow of the cerebrospinal fluid began with it springing forth predominantly from the lateral ventricles and flowing in a unidirectional pattern through a series

---

[142] Telano, *Physiology, Cerebral Spinal Fluid.*
[143] L. Sakka, G. Coll, J. Chazal, "Anatomy and Physiology of Cerebrospinal Fluid," *European Annals of Otorhinolaryngology, Head and Neck Diseases* 128, no. 6 (December 2011), doi:10.1016/j.anorl.2011.03.002.
[144] L. Sakka, "Anatomy and Physiology of Cerebrospinal Fluid."
[145] L. Sakka, "Anatomy and Physiology of Cerebrospinal Fluid."

of foramens and ventricles in the brain. After flowing through the brain's interior cavities, a portion of the CSF enters the spinal column for circulation around the spinal cord, the rest making its way to bathe the exterior part of the brain. Finally, the reabsorption of the CSF occurs "through outpouchings into the superior sagittal sinus (SSS) known as the arachnoid granulations."[146] The above description was intentionally vague because modern research shows CSF does not flow in a unidirectional pattern.[147] While the function of the ventricles, foramina, and arachnoid granulations is still relevant, modern imaging technology offers new insight into fluid movement.

The use of magnetic resonance imaging (MRIs), myelograms, and cisternography allows for the study of cerebrospinal fluid motion. As a result of the technology, several studies involve using MRIs to show links between the flow of CSF and influencing factors such as "arterial and venous blood flow, heart rate, blood pressure, and respiration."[148] The primary influences are "blood circulation and respiration under normal conditions."[149] Also, a new hypothesis regarding CSF physiology is emerging. "CSF movement is not presented as a circulation, but a permanent

---

[146] Ahmad H. Khasawneh et al. "Cerebrospinal fluid circulation: What do we know and how do we know it?," *Brain Circulation* vol. 4, no. 1 (2018), doi:10.4103/bc.bc_3_18.
[147] Klarica, Marijan, Milan Rados, Darko Oreskovic, "The Movement of Cerebrospinal Fluid and Its Relationship with Substances Behavior in Cerebrospinal and Interstitial Fluid" *Neuroscience* vol. 414, no. 21 (Aug. 2019). https://doi.org.10.1016/j.neuroscience.2019.06.032.
[148] Claudia Stirk MD, Uwe Klose PhD, Michael Erb, PhD, Herwig Strik, MD, and Wolfgang Grodd, MD, "Intracranial Oscillations of Cerebrospinal Fluid and Blood Flows: Analysis With Magnetic Resonance Imaging," *Journal of Magnetic Resonance Imaging,* vol. 15 (2002), doi:10.1002/jmri.10084.
[149] Shigeki Yamada, Masatsune Ishikawa, and Kazuhiko Nozaki, "Exploring mechanisms of ventricular enlargement in idiopathic normal pressure hydrocephalus: a role of cerebrospinal fluid dynamics and motile cilia" *Fluids Barriers CNS,* vol. 18, no. 20 (April 19, 2021), doi: 10.1186/s12987-021-00243-6.

rhythmic systolic–diastolic pulsation in all directions."[150] Supporting the phenomena is that cerebral spinal fluid travels in an environment free of valves. "Like venous circulation, CSF circulation depends upon indirect and passive mechanisms to propel cephalad flow. But unlike the veins, the SAS (subarachnoid space) contains no valves to prevent backflow, and both caudad and cephalad flow of CSF may occur simultaneously in the spinal SAS."[151]

Oscillating movement allows for the CSF to distribute substances in numerous different directions. The central nervous system's microvessels clean the CSF with "transport mechanisms" that facilitate the removal of unnecessary substances. Located in interstitial fluid compartments, the compartments "communicate freely" and "If a certain transport mechanism is not available at one site, the substance CSF movement along with the CSF system and into the CNS region where that transport mechanism is available."[152]

Furthermore, in a study titled "Cerebrospinal Fluid Physiology: Visualization of Cerebrospinal Fluid Dynamics Using the Magnetic Resonance Imaging Time-Spatial Inversion Pulse Method" scientist observed "CSF simply starts to move toward the location where it can flow more easily with little resistance."[153] A participant lying in a supine position result in CSF moving to the ventral side of the spinal column. Switching the same participant to a prone

---

[150] Klarica, "The Movement of Cerebrospinal Fluid and Its Relationship with Substances Behavior in Cerebrospinal and Interstitial Fluid."

[151] James M. Whedon and Donald Glassey, "Cerebrospinal fluid stasis and its clinical significance," *Alternative therapies in health and medicine* vol. 15, no. 3 (2009), https://www.ncbi.nlm.nih.gov/pmc/articles/PMC2842089/.

[152] Klarica, "The Movement of Cerebrospinal Fluid and Its Relationship with Substances Behavior in Cerebrospinal and Interstitial Fluid."

[153] Shinya Yamada, "Cerebrospinal fluid physiology: visualization of cerebrospinal fluid dynamics using the magnetic resonance imaging Time-Spatial Inversion Pulse method," *Croatian medical journal* vol. 55, no. 4 (2014), doi:10.3325/cmj.2014.55.337.

position result in the fluid pulsing primarily along the dorsal side of the spinal column.[154] This study leaves one to conclude that posture concerning gravity affects CSF movement.

Now that we have established a basic understanding of CSF movement let's consider what manifests when the cerebrospinal fluid lacks movement. J.M. Whedon and D. Glassey's article "Cerebrospinal fluid stasis and its clinical significance" explores this side of CSF health. They concluded, "CSF stasis may be associated with adverse mechanical cord tension, vertebral subluxation syndrome, reduced cranial rhythmic impulse, and restricted respiratory function." [155] Additionally, they surmised, "in most adults over the age of 30, however, the central canal is probably not patent (unobstructed, free of passage)." As the spinal canal acquires permanent obstructions, the result is a condition known as spinal stenosis. As a result of the presence of the obstruction, the spinal column narrows and can lead to classic signs of aging such as "back pain, weakness or numbness of the legs and loss of bowel or bladder control."[156] One may ask, "What actions can we take to avoid such a fate?" Perhaps *The Khecarividya of Adinatha's* explanation offers the most accessible answer.

XII Cerebrospinal Fluid Breathing/Bandhās

The pre-Medieval Transformation method for moving *Kuṇḍalinī* includes the phrase

---

154 Yamada, "Cerebrospinal fluid physiology: visualization of cerebrospinal fluid dynamics using the magnetic resonance imaging Time-Spatial Inversion Pulse method," doi:10.3325/cmj.2014.55.337.

155 James M. Whedon and Donald Glassey, "Cerebrospinal fluid stasis and its clinical significance," *Alternative therapies in health and medicine* vol. 15, no. 3 (2009), www.ncbi.nlm.nih.gov/pmc/articles/PMC2842089/.

156 Paul W. Hodges et al. "Intra-abdominal pressure increases stiffness of the lumbar spine." *Journal of biomechanics* vol. 38, no. 9 (2005), doi:10.1016/j.jbiomech.2004.08.016.

upward impulses of the breath (*ūrdhvaretāḥ)* (the yogin) should awaken the sleeping goddess *Kuṇḍalinī* whose abode is the base (and) whose form is like a lotus fiber."[157]

We now know "During inspiration, increased abdominal pressure causes an influx of blood into the lumbar spinal canal that increases the extradural pressure (Usubiaga *et al.* 1967) and compresses the dural sac, thus displacing CSF rostrally (Du Boulay *et al.* 1972; Martins *et al.* 1972)."[158] Additionally, Aktas notes "abdominal breathing clearly elicits higher flow rates during forced respiration (abdominal breathing) compared to thoracic breathing."[159] Is it possible that *yogi's* physical experience of evoking *Kuṇḍalinī* with breath occurred due to a sensitivity to CSF's upward trajectory towards the brain?

Mahabandā concerns itself with

Contract the anus and yoni and make the apana move upwards. 37

Join prana with samana and make it face downwards, the wise yogi should apply this in order to make prana and apana move upwards. 38[160]

On the exterior of the spinal column runs an epidural artery and an epidural vein. According to researcher Robert Lloyd "during inspiration, there is an influx of epidural blood directed towards the thoracic spinal canal from both the cervical and lumbar spine."[161] Concurrently we

---

157 Mallinson, *The Khecarīvidyā of Ādinātha, 28.*

158 G. Aktas, J.M. Kollmeier, A.A. Joseph *et al.*, "Spinal CSF flow in response to forced thoracic and abdominal respiration," *Fluids Barriers CNS* vol. 16, no. 10 (2019). https://doi.org/10.1186/s12987-019-0130-0.

159 Aktas, "Spinal CSF flow in response to forced thoracic and abdominal respiration."

160 James Mallinson, ed. *The Śiva Saṁhitā* (Woodstock, New York: Yoga Vidya, 2007), 81.

161 Robert Lloyd, Jane Butler, Simon C. Gandevia, and Iain K. Ball, "Respiratory cerebrospinal fluid flow is driven by the thoracic and lumbar spinal pressures," *The Journal of Physiology*, 598, no. 24 (October 2020), DOI: 10.1113/JP279458.

understand that inhalation raises the intraabdominal pressure (IAP), which raises the intrathoracic pressure. "This causes an increase in backpressure in the jugular veins and decreased drainage of venous blood and CSF."[162] Also as noted above, increasing the IAP results in the CSF moving rostrally. Perhaps this physiological chain of events leads to Yogi's experiencing "all the fluids in the vessels of the body of the Yogi are propelled up towards the head" and "the wind enters the middle channel of the *Suṣumanā."*[163]

Could it be possible the stimulation of CSF stirs up unnecessary substances increasing the efficiency of transport mechanisms "removal of brain metabolism waste products, such as peroxidation products, glycosylated proteins, excess neurotransmitters, debris from the lining of the ventricles, bacteria, viruses, and otherwise unnecessary molecules" found in CSF, thus becoming a preventative measure for the onset of spinal stenosis? [164] Spinal stenosis is a primary factor in decreasing an individual's longevity.[165] Could this be a modern interpretation to The *Haṭha Yoga Pradīpikā 's* stating "even an old person can become young" by using *mula bandhā*?[166] Additionally, the fluid's movement facilities the transportation of vitamins B1 and B12. These vitamins are necessary for a healthy nervous system, and folate for red and white blood cell production in the bone marrow. Studies show that there is an association of "folate, vitamin B12, and vitamin B6 with fracture incidence in older adults."[167] Perhaps the healthy

---

162 Lloyd, , "Respiratory cerebrospinal fluid flow is driven by the thoracic and lumbar spinal pressures," DOI: 10.1113/JP279458.
163 Vasu, *The Śiva Saṁhitā*, 60-61.

164 Telano, "Physiology, Cerebral Spinal Fluid. [Updated 2021 Jul 9]. In: StatPearls [Internet]: www.ncbi.nlm.nih.gov/books/NBK519007.
165 Hodges et al. "Intra-abdominal pressure increases stiffness of the lumbar spine."
166 Muktibodhananda, *Hatha Yoga Pradipika*, 348.

167 Tao he, Xiangyn Jin, Yee Sin Koh, Quingyu Zhang, Chao Zhang, Fanxiao Liu, "The association of homocysteine, folate, vitamin B12, and vitamin B6 with fracture incidence in

fluid flow of cerebrospinal fluid (CSF) assists with making "the skeleton strong" as stated in the *Śiva Saṃhitā* under ***Mahābandhā***.[168] *Mahābandhā* also mechanically creates more intrabdominal pressure (IAP) by placing the heel on the perineum and contacting the muscles associated with lifting the pelvic floor. Pressing the heel creates pressure that causes the CSF to move up towards the head. The foundational posture stabilizes the back and creates space for the more intense posture *uḍḍīyāna bandhā.*

As found in the *Haṭha* texts, *mula bandhā* is a precursor for *uḍḍāna bandhā.* Interestingly, Jacek Cholewicki's paper "Can Increased Intra-Abdominal Pressure in Humans be Decoupled from Trunk Muscles Contraction During Steady State Isometric Extertions" concludes that it is not possible to muscularly separate the action of creating intraabdominal pressure and intrathoracic pressure. Both types of engagement are dependent on the other. In this light, *uḍḍāna bandhā* is dependent on *mula bandhā.* The action of lifting the diaphragm up under the rib cage intensifies posture as it raises and hugs the intestines to the spine. In addition to the stated advantages of *mula bandhā, uḍḍāna bandhā* includes stimulating the digestive fires and increasing the body's fluids. As the *Śiva Saṃhitā Uḍḍāna bandha* states

> The fire in his stomach burns brightly and there is an increase in his vital fluids. 75[169]

---

older adults: a systematic review and meta-analysis." *Annals of Translational Medicine,* vol. 9, no. 4 (July 2021), doi: 10.21037/atm-21-2514.

[168] James Mallinson, ed. *The Śiva Saṁhitā* (Woodstock, New York: Yoga Vidya, 2007), 81.

[169] Mallinson, ed. *The Śiva Saṁhitā*, 91.

Studies have shown visceral massage assists with digestion, elimination, gas, and reflux.[170]

Finally, we come to *jālandhara bandhā*. *Jālandhara bandhā* concerns itself with protecting "the nectar which exudes of the thousand-petalled lotus" from digestive juices and stopping the cessation of the *ida* and *pingala*, which are like *apāna vāyu and prāna vāyu.*[171] Once again, the rationale applied to *mula-bandhā* applies to this *bandhā* as well. Contraction of the throat muscles and lowering the chin to the chest stimulates the phrenic nerves causing "Intra-abdominal pressure (to) increase(s) the stiffness of the lumbar spine."[172] Additionally, Paul Hodges found one can increase the intra-abdominal pressure by using tetanic stimulation of the phrenic nerves "without concurrent activity of the abdominal and back extensor muscles."[173] Through physical means, *jālandhara bandhā* assists the Yogi to sit up straight and align the spine so the cerebrospinal fluid can optimally move in a caudal direction.

Again, the practice of *Kundalini* cultivates a body capable of manifesting vitality through the proper distribution of *prāṇa.* If there is a correlation between the movement of *kuṇḍalinī* and CSF, with CSF being a vehicle to transport *prāṇa*, the highways that it travels on are the *nāḍī*. We have discussed the three main *nāḍī*: *ida, pingala, and sushumna*, but have yet to address what may comprise the 350,000 *nāḍī* as mentioned in the *Haṭha Yoga Pradīpikā*.

---

170 H. Liu, B. Yu, M. Zhang, K. Liu, F. C. Wang, & X. Y. Gao, (2015). "Treatment of Diabetic Gastroparesis by Complementary and Alternative Medicines," *Medicines,* vol. 2, no. 3. (Basel, Switzerland, April 16, 2021), https://doi.org/10.3390/medicines2030212.

171 Vasu, *The Śiva Saṁhitā*, 64.
172 Hodges et al. "Intra-abdominal pressure increases stiffness of the lumbar spine."
173 Hodges et al. "Intra-abdominal pressure increases stiffness of the lumbar spine."

According to the 73rd passage on *jālandhara bandhā,*

> By firmly contracting the throat, the two nadis, ida and pingala are paralyzed and the sixteen adharas of the middle chakra[174] [175] are locked.[176]

The *Siddha-siddhanta paddhati* or "text of Gorakhshanath" states the sixteen *adharas* (points) in the human body "can lead to the emergence of qualitative pratyahara, as well as the awakening of the sushumna and Kundalini-shakti."[177] Natha initiate, Yogi Matsyendranath Maharaj lists the sixteen *adharas* as such.

1. *Padangushta-adhara* – the toes.
2. *Muladhara* - is the perineum, the muladhara-chakra
3. *Gudadhara* -the anus.
4. *Medbradhara* – the base of the genital, svadhishthana-chakra
5. *Uddiyana-adhara*- kanda, lower abdomen
6. *Nadhi-adhara* – the naval area, manipura-chakra
7. *Hridaya-adhara* – the area of the heart, anahata-chakra
8. *Kantha-adhara* – the area of the neck, vishuddha-chakra
9. *Ghantika-adhara* – uvula.
10. *Talu-adhara* – soft palate, talu-chakra.[178] [179]

---

[174] Middle chakra refers to the *visuddha* (throat) chakra and sometimes the *muladhara* (root) chakra, according to *Siddha-siddhanta paddhati.*
[175] "Adhara." Natha Tradition. Nathas.org. 2022.
[176] Muktibodhananda, *Hatha Yoga Pradipika*, 356.
[177] "Adhara." Natha Tradition. Nathas.org. 2022.
[178] Talu-chakra (palate-chakra)- locate in the soft palate, it relates to Bindu and Vishuddha-chakra. "After the nectar leaves Bindu and before reaching Visuddha, it remains in Talu-chakra."
[179] "Talu-chakra." Natha Tradition. Nathas.org. 2022.

11. Jihva-adhara – tongue.

12. Bhrumadhya-adhara – the area between the eyebrows, ajna chakra.

13. Nasa-adhara – the tip of the nose

14. Kapata-adhara – the base of the nose.

15. Lalata-adhara – the center of the forehead.

16. Brahmarandhra-adhara – brahmarandhra, akasha-chakra[180]

It is here that our conversation begins to come full circle. As we can see, the list of the sixteen *adharas,* includes references to *cakras*. We are recalling modern guru B.K.S. Iyengar and researcher Charles W. Leadbeater's interpretation of the *chakras* with nerve plexus[181] and reflecting on the striking parallels between the locations of the sixteen *adharas* and twelve cranial nerves evokes a curiosity regarding the relationship between the nerves and the concept of the *nāḍī.* Each of the twelve cranial nerves will have one, two, or three characteristics classified as sensory function, somatic function, and parasympathetic motor function (PMF). We will review them according to the text *Anatomy and Physiology, An Integrative Approach.*[182]

1. Olfactory – <u>Sensory</u>: smell.
2. Optic – <u>Sensory</u>: vision.

---

[180] *Akasha-chakra* (throat chakra).
[181] It begins with the coccyx or *muladhara* (root) *chakra* near the sacral plexus. It innervates testes and relates to L1-L3 sympathetic and S3-S4 parasympathetic. From the base we move up to L1 to the *svadhisthana.* L1 is the hypogastric plexus which innervates the pancreas, ovaries, and intestines. Next is T8, or *manipura*/celiac plexus, innervating the adrenals, diaphragm, and skin. Then T1, *anhata*/cardiac plexus, innervating the heart, thymus, lungs, and lymph glands. Moving up to C3, *vishuddha*/pharyngeal plexus, innervating thyroid, parathyroid, throat, and eyes. C1, *ajna*/nasociliary plexus, innervates the pituitary, pineal, brain and ears. Finally, the crown of the head, *sahasrana*, which fully encompasses the cerebral cortex.
[182] Michael P. McLinley, Valerie Dean O'Loughlin, Theresa Stouter Bidle, *Anatomy & Physiology, An Integrative Approach,* New York, New York; McGraw Hill, (2013), 522.

3. Oculomotor – Somatic: control four extrinsic eye muscles. PMF: pupil constriction and construction of ciliary muscles to make eye more rounded.
4. Trochlear – Somatic: control superior oblique eye muscles.
5. Trigeminal – Sensory: anterior scalp, nasal cavity, nasopharynx, entire face, most of oral cavity, teeth, anterior two-thirds of the tongue; part of auricle ear, meninges. Somatic: muscles of mastication, mylohyoid, digastric (anterior belly), tensor tympani, tensor veli palatini.
6. Abducens – Somatic: lateral rectus eye muscle.
7. Facial – Sensory: tastes from the anterior two-thirds of tongue. Somatic: muscles of facial expression, digastric (posterior belly), stylohyoid, stapedius. PMF: increase secretion from the lacrimal gland of eye, submandibular and the sublingual salivary glands.
8. Vestibulocochlear – Sensory: hearing (cochlear branch); equilibrium (vestibular branch).
9. Glossopharyngeal – Sensory: general sensory and taste to posterior one-third of the tongue, general sensory to part of the pharynx. Visceral sensory from the carotid bodies. Somatic: one pharyngeal muscle (stylopharyngeus). PMF: Increases secretion from the parotid salivary glands.
10. Vagus – Sensory: visceral sensory information from the heart, lungs, liver, gallbladder, stomach, pancreas, spleen, large intestine, small intestine, rectum, kidney, urinary bladder, penis/scrotum, ovary/uterus. General sensory information from external acoustic meatus, tympanic membrane, part of the pharynx, laryngopharynx, and larynx. Somatic: most pharyngeal muscles; all laryngeal

muscles. PMF: innervates smooth muscle and glands of the heart, lungs, larynx, trachea, and most abdominal organs. Accessory – Somatic: trapezius muscle, sternocleidomastoid muscle.

11. Accessory – Somatic: Trapezius muscle, sternocleidomastoid muscle
12. Hypoglossal – Somatic: intrinsic and extrinsic tongue muscles.

Steaming from the vagus nerve are the main four main nerve plexuses. They are the cervical plexus (for the head, neck, and shoulders),[183] brachial plexus (for the chest, shoulders, arms and hands),[184] lumbar plexus (for the back, abdomen, groin, thighs, knees, and calves), [185] and the sacral plexus (for the pelvis, buttocks, genitals, thighs, calves, and feet).[186] We find ourselves back to possible correlation between the *cakras* and the 12 cranial nerves with a possible further connection. The *Haṭha Yoga Pradīpikā's* 72nd and 73rd passage on *jālandhara bandhā* states.

> Having done Jalandhara bandha by contracting the throat, the nectar does not fall into the gastric fire and the prana is not agitated.
> By firmly contracting the throat, the two nadis, ida and pingala are paralyzed and the sixteen adharas of the middle chakra and locked.[187]

The June of 2021 original research study "All Central Nervous System Neuro- and Vascular- Communication Channels Are Surrounded with Cerebrospinal Fluid" states, "To our

---

183 McLinley, *Anatomy & Physiology, An Integrative Approach*, 552.
184 McLinley, 554.
185 McLinley, 559.
186 McLinley, 563.
187 Muktibodhananda, *Hatha Yoga Pradipika*, 356.

knowledge, this is the first study to simultaneously and systematically verify that all 12 pairs of cranial nerves, all MRI-visible vasculature, and spinal nerves are surrounded with CSF *in vivo* in humans; as opposed to previous studies that have asynchronously investigated this, mainly in animals and human cadavers. Our findings indicate that all brain parenchyma and spinal cord communication channels, both neuro- and vascular-communication channels, are encased in CSF."[188] The original research challenges the belief that CSF is exclusive the central nervous system with the exception of the optic nerve.[189] This means all the CSF encased cranial nerves either remain in the head or have to pass down through the neck to reach the rest of the body. If we think of the cranial nerve sheaths as hoses with water flowing through them, could "firmly contacting the throat," kink the CSF hoses and suspend the passage of the CSF from the head down into the body? Would this action increase fluid to the *Talu-chakra,* or soft palate? Can an imbalance of CSF in sheaths lead to disorders?

A little insight into last question comes from a study entitled "Cerebrospinal fluid and optic nerve sheath compartment syndrome: A common pathophysiological mechanism in five different cases?"[190] The study of five individuals found "Compartmentation of the ONS (optic nerve sheath) demonstrated by contrast-loaded CT cisternography was the consistent finding in all five patients who demonstrated findings of ON (optic nerve) dysfunction. The aetiologias

---

[188] Lara M. Fahmy, Yongsheng Chen, Stepanie Xuan, E. Mark Haacke, Jiani Hu, and Quan Jiang, "All Central Nervous System Neuro – and Vascular – Communication Channels Are Surrounded with Cerebrospinal Fluid," *Frontiers in Neurology,* (June 17, 2021), original research: https://doi.org/10.3389/fneur.2021.614636.

[189] J. Hao, A. Pircher, N.R. Miller., J. Hsieh, L. Remonda, & H.E. Killer, "Cerebrospinal fluid and optic nerve sheath compartment syndrome: A common pathophysiological mechanism in five different cases?," *Clinical & experimental ophthalmology*, vol. 48, no. 2, (2020) 212–219: https://doi.org/10.1111/ceo.13663.

[190] Pircher, "Cerebrospinal fluid and optic nerve sheath compartment syndrome: A common pathophysiological mechanism in five different cases?"

varied and included meningitis, papilloedema, sphenoid wing meningioma, disc herniation and normal-tension glaucoma."[191] The original research on CSF in the peripheral nervous system further engrains my curiosity that studying the sophisticated development of "inner spiritual architecture" and philosophies from the traditions of *layayoga, kuṇḍalinīyoga,* and *haṭhayoga* offers unique and relevant insights for multidimensional whole-body research.

Considering CSF under the *pañcamayakośa* model allows for exploring the fluid's role in our body, breath, mind, emotions, and spirituality. Let us recall that Gopi Krishna likened a negative *kuṇḍalinī* awakening to the experience to a sudden "increase in the flow of blood to the brain" which can cause "faintness, complete insensibility, excitement, irritability, or in extreme cases, delirium, paralysis, or death."[192] Could an increase in understanding of *Kuṇḍalinī* through the lens of the *pañcamayakośa* model provide insight to CSF? Is it possible the techniques for raising *Kuṇḍalinī* could provide individuals with tools for auras, migraines, dissociative states, ringing of the ears, and altered vision due to autism, encephalitis hydrocephalus, and spinal stenosis?[193] [194] [195] [196]

---

[191] Pircher, ""Cerebrospinal fluid and optic nerve sheath compartment syndrome: A common pathophysiological mechanism in five different cases?"

[192] Gopi Krishna, *Living with Kundalini, The Autobiography of Gopi Krishna* (Boston, Massachusetts: Shambhala Publications, 1993), 143.

[193] "Autism Spectrum Disorder (ASD)." Center for Disease Control and Prevention. March 2022. www.cdc.gov/ncbddd/autism/signs.html.

[194] "Encephalitis" Mayo Clinic. April 2020. www.mayoclinic.org/diseases/encephalitis.

[195] "Hydrocephalus" Mayo Clinic. September 2021. www.mayoclinic.org/diseases/hydrocephalus.

[196] "Spinal Stenosis" Mayo Clinic. October 2020. www.mayoclinic.org/diseases/spinal-stenosis.

XIII A Story of Encephalitis

While researching for my thesis in the fall of 2021 my friend, Louis van Breemen, informed me that a former student, Taylor Harrington, was diagnosed with encephalitis. Fortunately, the young woman's roommate recognized her symptoms due to reading the autobiography about encephalitis entitled "Brain on Fire: My Month of Madness" by Susannah Cahalan.[197] The roommate's familiarity with the symptoms motivated her to call 911. After being rushed to a nearby New York City emergency room, she immediately received clearance to undergo lifesaving surgery. According to Cedars Sinai, "Encephalitis is inflammation and swelling of the brain. This leads to changes in neurological function. It can result in mental confusion and seizures."[198] Viruses are the leading cause of the disease and symptoms can include changes in alertness, hallucinations, sleepiness or lethargy, personality changes, double vision, loss of appetite, confusion, weakness of arms and legs, impaired hearing and speech, headaches, seizures, coma etc.[199] Unfortunately, while healing many of symptoms persist as side effects.

Upon reconnecting with Taylor, it was to my amazement many of the things she found challenging were discussed in "Living with Kundalini" by Gopi Krishna during the unfolding of his *Kundalini* experience. Although she did not experience a *kuṇḍalinī* awakening or an increase of CSF, as with the occurrence of hydrocephalus,[200] "The deleterious consequences of

---

[197] Susannah Cahalan, *Brain on Fire: My Month of Madness*, (Free Press, November 13, 2012).
[198] "Encephalitis," Cedars-Sinai, March 27, 2022, www.cedars-sinai.org/health-library/diseases-and-conditions/e/encephalitis.html.
[199] "Encephalitis," Cedars-Sinai.
[200] According to the National Institute of Neurological Disorders and Stroke, hydrocephalus is defined as "an abnormal buildup of fluid in the ventricles (cavities) deep within the brain" and asserts that "when the normal flow or absorption of CSF is blocked it can result in a buildup of CSF. The pressure from too much CSF can keep the brain from functioning properly and cause brain damage and even death."[200]

unchecked inner cranial pressure (IPC) highlight the importance of maintaining ICP homeostasis within the central nervous system (CNS). Cerebrospinal fluid (CSF) is an important component of maintaining a stable ICP, and disruptions to secretion or drainage can lead to ICP elevations."[201] Taylor's ICP disruption was the result of increased blood flow to the brain that disrupted the intracranial fluid balance. As stated by Krishna her "increase in the flow of blood to the brain" resulted in "faintness, complete insensibility, excitement, irritability, or in extreme cases, delirium, temporary paralysis, and (almost her) death."[202]

She still experiences auras[203] and occasional seizures.[204] Despite the adverse side effects from slipping into the alternate states of consciousness, she shared, "I find the experiences appealing, and it is as if there is a profound message that is trying to be said to me, a fully realized thought, that if I just listen openly it will result in a transformational experience."[205] There have been times when she did "let herself go" and temporarily "slipped into a coma-like state" which afterward resulted in "seeing glowing light around objects," "feeling like I am in the world but not a part of it," "having a tough time focusing," and sometimes "losing my balance and wanting to get low or on the ground to stabilize."[206]

As a young woman in her 20's Taylor is ready to "get back to normal" and carry on with her life. While talking about the *pañcamayakośa* model and *kuṇḍalinī* she voluntarily elected to

---

201 S.W. Bothwell, D. Janigro, & A. Patabendige, "Cerebrospinal fluid dynamics and intracranial pressure elevation in neurological diseases," *Fluids Barriers CNS* 16, no. 9 (2019). https://doi.org/10.1186/s12987-019-0129-6.
202 Krishna, *Living with Kundalini,* 143.
203 According to Mayoclinic.org, an aura can "be sensory, motor, or verbal disturbances. Visual auras are most common. – A visual aura is like an electrical or chemical wave that moves across the visual cortex of your brain. The visual cortex is the part of your brain that processes visual signals. As the wave spreads, you might have visual hallucinations."
204 Taylor Harrington, Zoom Conversation, Feb. 23, 2022.
205 Harrington, Zoom Conversation, Feb. 23, 2022.
206 Harrington, Zoom Conversation, Feb. 23, 2022.

ask her doctor's permission to try a few techniques suggested in *Living with Kundalini.*[207] She is now eating a little something every three hours and enjoys alternate nostril breathing. When in public, she finds being aware of her breath increases her sense of stability and helps her regain her equilibrium and focus confronted with an aura. Mentally, she finds the physical techniques help her emotionally by quieting her mind, which relaxes her nerves and helps her feel more in control. She shared having the tools help her engage in everyday activities going to the store. She finds solace in knowing that if she starts to have an "episode" she can try the tools to gain balance.[208] Taylor is aware of *kuṇḍalinī's* tradition to foster a genius state of mind and is not opposed to the possibility; however, more immediately, she notes her experience in the hospital evoked a peace of mind so profound she is "no longer afraid to die."[209] She likens the events as "profoundly spiritual experiences."[210]

Since engaging with techniques used by Gopi Krishna during his journey with *kundalini*, she feels her symptoms have become more manageable, and her medication levels are lowering as her activity levels are increasing. This is not to say it is the techniques that have made the difference; however, our conversations offered additional perspectives to her medical care. They revolved around the intrinsic connection between her body, breath, mind, emotions, and spirit. Additionally, the conversations lead to self-exploration, self-care, and empowerment at a time when her reliance on doctors and medicine left her feeling "out of control of her reality."[211]

The interpretation of the traditional texts through the lens of eastern philosophy and religion negates bypassing the literature as symbolic poetry void of practical advice or ancient

---

207 Harrington, Feb. 23, 2022.
208 Taylor Harrington, Zoom Conversation, April 6, 2022.
209 Harrington, April 6, 2022.
210 Harrington, April 6, 2022.
211 Harrington, Feb. 23, 2022.

practices with little relevancy given our advances in modern medicine. Undeniably evidence-based medicine's unprecedented advancements in health care are unparalleled; however, as curious and intelligent beings, it is only natural that we perpetually manifest our understanding of the human experience to lead inspired lives. George L. Engel is a modern example of a notable American internist and psychiatrist who benefited from embracing a multidimensional health model, which ultimately led to his creation of the biopsychosocial model.[212] Naturally, Engel's 45-year-old model is not without criticism; however, his curious exploration of a discipline seemingly unrelated to his primary field of study led to an integrated model that continues to inform the studies of arts and sciences in new directions.[213] Additionally the model itself has evolved to become the biopsychosocial-spiritual model.[214] While this development is exciting it still omits the importance of breath from a physical and subtle body standpoint. Perhaps we can take a note from the *Kaushitaki Upanishad, third adhyāya* verse three, when contemplating this point.

> 3. One lives with speech gone, for we see the dumb;
>
> one lives with eye gone, for we see the blind;
>
> one lives with ear gone, for we see the deaf;
>
> one lives with mind gone, for we see the childish;
>
> one lives with arms cuts off, one lives with legs cut off, for thus we see.

---

212 G. Papadimitriou, "The "Biopsychosocial Model": 40 years of application in Psychiatry," *Psychiatrike = Psychiatriki*, vol. *28*, no. 2, 107–110 (2017), https://doi.org/10.22365/jpsych.2017.282.107

213 Papadimitriou, "The "Biopsychosocial Model": 40 years of application in Psychiatry."

214 M. Saad, A. C. Mosini, "Are We Ready for a True Biopsychosocial-Spiritual Model? The Many Meanings of "Spiritual"," *Medicines,* Basel, Switzerland, vol. 4, no. 4, 79 (2017), https://doi.org/10.3390/medicines4040079.

> But now it is the breath spirit (*prāṇa*), even the intelligential self (*prajñātman*), that seizes hold of and animates (*ut-thā*) this body. This, therefore, one should reverence as Uktha.[215] [216]

XIV Conclusion

The focus of this thesis is to explore "the inner spiritual architecture" through the lens of the *pañcamayakośa* model concerning raising *kuṇḍalinī.* By learning more about the history and relationship between the *brahmānanda vallī/pañcamayakośa* model, "the inner spiritual architecture," *bandhās*, and *kuṇḍalinī* we come to appreciate the unique perspectives on the functioning of the human body. Cultivating a greater understanding of *prāṇa, nāḍī,* and *cakra* places emphasis on the role of *mula bandhā uḍḍīyāna bandhā, jālandhara bandhā,* and *mahabandā*, in directly influencing the state of ones "inner spiritual architecture." Additionally, familiarization of *bandhā's* through the *Śiva Saṃhitā, Haṭha Yoga Pradīpikā*, and *Gheraṇḍa Saṃhitā* reveals the techniques serve multidimensional purposes. By considering the tradition of raising *kuṇḍalinī* from the *pañcamayakośa'* model we can gain multiple points of reference for comparing the esoteric practice to the form, function, and flow of cerebrospinal fluid (CSF).

The investigation found the four *bandhā's* impact CSFs in a way that is congruent with the recorded sensations associated with *kuṇḍalinī* rising. Additionally, the benefits affiliated with practice of raising *kuṇḍalinī* match the health benefits gained from free-flowing CSF. Finally, the recorded negative side effects affiliated with raising *kuṇḍalinī* parallel the side effects of CSF in stasis. My goal is not to define the spiritual practice of *kuṇḍalinī.* Instead, it is to understand the

---

215 'The Recitation of Praise' in the ritual.

216 Hume, 322.

tradition of raising *kuṇḍalinī* in its entirety to provide possible unique perspectives for diseases and disorders that affect the central and peripheral nervous system. A Bioplumonarypsychosocial-Spiritual pursuit if you will. I hope this curiosity-based inquiry highlights some advantages of studying *yogic* philosophy in a way that honors the original texts, inspires transformation of thought, and opens unique ways to pursue a life full of vitality.

Bibliography

Anodea Judith. *Chakra Balancing Kit: A Guide to Healing and Awakening your Energy Field.* Boulder, CO: Sounds True, 2003.

Aktas, G., J. M. Kollmeier, A. A. Joseph, *et al.* "Spinal CSF flow in response to forced thoracic and abdominal respiration." *Fluids Barriers CNS* 16, no. 10 (2019). https://doi.org/10.1186/s12987-019-0130-0.

Bothwell, S.W., D. Janigro, & A. Patabendige. "Cerebrospinal fluid dynamics and intracranial pressure elevation in neurological diseases." *Fluids Barriers CNS* 16, no. 9 (2019). https://doi.org/10.1186/s12987-019-0129-6.

Cahalan, Susannah. *Brain on Fire: My Month of Madness*. Glencoe, Illinois: Free Press, November 13, 2012.

Chapple, Christopher Key. *Yoga and the Luminous, Patañjali's Spiritual Path to Freedom.* Delhi, India: Divine Books, 2008.

Chapple, Christopher Key. *Yoga in Jainism*. New York, New York: Routledge, 2017.

Center for Disease Control and Prevention. "Autism Spectrum Disorder (ASD)." Accessed April, 27, 2022. cdc.gov/ncbddd/autism/signs.html.

Colomer-Sánchez, Ana et al. "Anxiety Effect on Communication Skills in Nursing Supervisors: An Observational Study." *Nursing reports* 11, no. 2 (Apr. 2021). doi:10.3390/nursrep11020021.

Cedars-Sinai. "Encephalitis." Accessed March 27, 2022. cedars-sinai.org/health-library/diseases-and-conditions/e/encephalitis.html.

Ernst, Carl W. *Yoga in Practice.* Edited by David Gordon White. Princeton, New Jersey: Princeton University Press, 2012.

Feuerstein, Georg Ph.D. *The Yoga Tradition: Its History, Literature, Philosophy, and Practice.* Chino Valley, Arizona: Hohm Press, 2008.

Flood, Gavin. *The Tantric Body: The Secret Tradition of Hindu Religion.* London: I.B. Tauris, 2006.

Fahmy, Lara M., Yongsheng Chen, Stepanie Xuan, E. Mark Haacke, Jiani Hu, and Quan Jiang, "All Central Nervous System Neuro – and Vascular – Communication Channels Are Surrounded with Cerebrospinal Fluid." *Frontiers in Neurology,* original research (June 17, 2021). https://doi.org/10.3389/fneur.2021.614636.

Gupta S., Gupta M. M. "Takotsubo Syndrome." *Indian Heart J.* 70, no. 1 (2018), doi:10.1016/j.ihj.2017.09.005.

Hao, J., A. Pircher, N.R. Miller., J. Hsieh, L. Remonda, & H.E. Killer. "Cerebrospinal fluid and optic nerve sheath compartment syndrome: A common pathophysiological mechanism in five different cases?" *Clinical & experimental ophthalmology* 48, no. 2 (2020). https://doi.org/10.1111/ceo.13663.

Harrington, Taylor. Zoom Conversation. Feb. 23, 2022.

Harrington, Taylor. Zoom Conversation, April 6, 2022.

He, Tao, Xiangyn Jin, Yee Sin Koh, Quingyu Zhang, Chao Zhang, Fanxiao Liu. "The association of homocysteine, folate, vitamin B12, and vitamin B6 with fracture incidence in older adults: a systematic review and meta-analysis." *Annals of Translational Medicine* 9, no. 4 (July 2021). doi: 10.21037/atm-21-2514.

Hui, Tay Li. "A systematic review on the factors affecting and the strategies to enhance effective communication between registered nurses and oncology adult patients in an inpatient setting." *JBI Library of Systematic Reviews* 7, no. 24 (2009). doi: 10.11124/jbisrir-2009-561.

Hume, Robert Ernest, ed. *The Thirteen Principal Upanishads, Translated from Sanskrit*. Oxford: Oxford University Press, 1983.

Johnston, Ian, Brian Owler, and John Pickard. *The Pseudotumor Cerebri Syndrome: Pseudotumor Cerebri, Idiopathic Intracranial Hyertension, Benign Intracranial Hypertnesion and Related Conditions.* Cambridge: Cambridge University Press, 2007. Ebook.

Khalsa, Hari Simran Kaur. Group conversation, 2010.

Khasawneh, Ahmad H. et al. "Cerebrospinal fluid circulation: What do we know and how do we know it?" *Brain Circulation* 4, no. 1 (2018). doi:10.4103/bc.bc_3_18.

Krishna, Gopi. *Living with Kundalini, The Autobiography of Gopi Krishna*. Boston, Massachusetts: Shambhala, 1993.

Lampert, Rachel. "ECG signatures of psychological stress." *Journal of electrocardiology* 48, no. 6 (2015). 1000-5. doi:10.1016/j.jelectrocard.2015.08.005.

Liu, H., B. Yu, M. Zhang, K. Liu, F. C. Wang, & X. Y. Gao. "Treatment of Diabetic Gastroparesis by Complementary and Alternative Medicines." *Medicines* 2, no. 3. (2015). https://doi.org/10.3390/medicines2030212.

Lloyd, Robert, Jane Butler, Simon C. Gandevia, and Iain K. Ball. "Respiratory cerebrospinal fluid flow is driven by the thoracic and lumbar spinal pressures." *The Journal of Physiology*, 598, no. 24 (October 2020). DOI: 10.1113/JP279458.

Mallinson, James. *The Khecarīvidyā of Ādinātha: A Critical Edition and Annotated Translation of an Early Text of Haṭhayoga.* London: Routledge, 2007.

Mallinson, James, Mark Singleton. *Roots of Yoga.* UK: Penguin Random House, 2017.

Mallinson, James. ed. *The Śiva Saṁhitā.* Woodstock, New York: Yoga Vidya, 2007.

Mallinson, James. *Yoga in Practice,* ed. David Gordon White. Princeton, New Jersey: Princeton University Press, 2012.

Marijan, Klarica, Milan Rados, Darko Oreskovic. "The Movement of Cerebrospinal Fluid and Its Relationship with Substances Behavior in Cerebrospinal and Interstitial Fluid." *Neuroscience* 414, no. 21 (Aug. 2019). https://doi.org.10.1016/j.neuroscience.2019.06.032.

McLinley, Michael P., Valerie Dean O'Loughlin, Theresa Stouter Bidle, *Anatomy & Physiology, An Integrative Approach,* New York, New York; McGraw Hill, (2013), 522.

Mayo Clinic. "Encephalitis." Accessed, April 27, 2022. www.mayoclinic.org/diseases/encephalitis.

Mayo Clinic. "Hydrocephalus." Accessed April 27, 2022. www.mayoclinic.org/diseases/hydrocephalus.

Mayo Clinic. "Spinal Stenosis." Accessed April 27, 2022. www.mayoclinic.org/diseases/spinal-stenosis.

Monier-Williams, Sir M. ed. A Sanskrit English Dictionary. Springfield, Virginia: Natara J. Books, 2017.

Muktibodhananda, Swami, Swami Satyananda Saraswati. *Hatha Yoga Pradipika 2013 Golden Jubilee Edition.* Bihar, India: Bihar School of Yoga, 2012.

Natha Tradition. "Adhara." Accessed April 24, 2022. Nathas.org. 2022.

Natha Tradition. "Talu-chakra." Accessed April 24, 2022. Nathas.org. 2022.

Namkhai, Chögyal Norbu. *Yantra Yoga, The Tibetan Yoga of Movement.* Boulder, Colorado: Snow Lion, 2008.

Papadimitriou, G. "The "Biopsychosocial Model": 40 years of application in Psychiatry." *Psychiatrike = Psychiatriki, 28*, no. 2 (2017), https://doi.org/10.22365/jpsych.2017.282.107.

Rele, Vasant G. *The Mysterious Kundalini, The Physical Basis of Kundalini Yoga In Terms of Western Anatomy and Physiology.* Agawam, Massachusetts: Silver Street Media, 2011.

Robin, Mel. *A Handbook for Yogasana Teachers, The Incorporation of Neuroscience, Physiology, and Anatomy into the Practice.* Tuscan, Azizona: Published by Wheatmark, 2009.

Saad, M., A. C. Mosini. "Are We Ready for a True Biopsychosocial-Spiritual Model? The Many Meanings of "Spiritual"." *Medicines* 4, no. 4 (2017), doi.org/10.3390/medicines4040079.

Sakka, L., G. Coll, J. Chazal. "Anatomy and Physiology of Cerebrospinal Fluid." *European Annals of Otorhinolaryngology, Head and Neck Diseases* 128, no. 6 (December 2011), doi:10.1016/j.anorl.2011.03.002.

Sarbacker, Stuart Ray. *Tracing the Path of Yoga, The History Philosophy of Indian Mind-Body Discipline*. Albany: State of University New York Press, 2021.

Stirk, Claudia MD, Uwe Klose PhD, Michael Erb, PhD, Herwig Strik, MD, and Wolfgang Grodd, MD. "Intracranial Oscillations of Cerebrospinal Fluid and Blood Flows: Analysis With Magnetic Resonance Imaging." *Journal of Magnetic Resonance Imaging* 15 (2002), doi:10.1002/jmri.10084.

Swami, Purnananda. *Sat-Chakra-Nirupana,* ed. Arthur Avalon. Expired copyright, Accessed February 11, 2022. http://omnamo.narod.ru/chakri.html (bahaistudies.net).

Telano, L.N., S. Baker, *Physiology, Cerebral Spinal Fluid.* Treasure Island, FL: State Pearls Publishing, July 4, 2020. Ebook.

Vasu, Rai Bahadur Srisa Chandra ed. *Gheraṇḍa Saṁhitā.* Varanasi, India: Indian Mind, 2012.

Whedon, James M. and Donald Glassey. "Cerebrospinal fluid stasis and its clinical significance." *Alternative therapies in health and medicine* 15, no. 3 (2009). https://www.ncbi.nlm.nih.gov/pmc/articles/PMC2842089/.

Yamada, Shigeki, Masatsune Ishikawa, and Kazuhiko Nozaki. "Exploring mechanisms of ventricular enlargement in idiopathic normal pressure hydrocephalus: a role of cerebrospinal fluid dynamics and motile cilia." *Fluids Barriers CNS* 18, no. 20 (April 19, 2021). doi: 10.1186/s12987-021-00243-6.

Zappaterra, Mauro. "The Cerebrospinal Fluid and I AM." YouTube. 2019. Educational Video, 31:33. https://youtu.be/oPU0DGjK3XA.

Milton Keynes UK
Ingram Content Group UK Ltd.
UKHW020252221123
432980UK00017B/1238

9 798868 989728